the maths collection

Kathie Barrs and Paul Briten

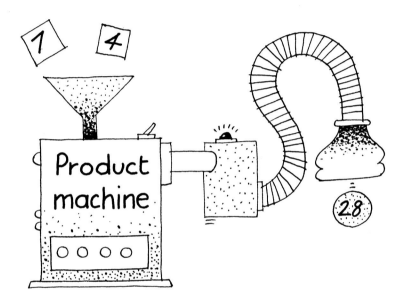

Line drawings by Tony Barrs

First Published in 1995 by
BELAIR PUBLICATIONS LIMITED
P.O. Box 12, Twickenham, England, TW1 2QL

© 1995 Kathie Barrs and Paul Briten
Series Editor Robyn Gordon
Designed by Richard Souper
Photography by Kelvin Freeman
Typesetting by Belair
Printed and Bound in Hong Kong through World Print Ltd
ISBN 0 947882 68 5

Acknowledgements

The Authors and Publishers would like to thank the children of Great Bardfield School, Braintree, Essex, for their contributions and support during the preparation of this book.

Contents

Introduction

The Maths Collection provides a series of varied ideas and suggestions which teachers will be able to incorporate into their lessons - regardless of the scheme or methods they are using.

Ideas are provided under major topic headings, and concepts are dealt with in the order that they are likely to be introduced. As suggested by the title, this book offers a collection of activities, each of which can be used independently to supplement a lesson. There are ideas to support children who encounter some difficulty with mathematics but, equally, many suggestions for extending all pupils including those who are most able. There are ideas for discussion to introduce topics, and each area covered is accompanied by suggestions for a display in the form of a colour photograph.

If required, the book can be used to provide a series of ideas to form the basis of a lesson or sequence of lessons at a suitable level within the particular topic.

To further extend the mathematics in an exciting manner, sixteen original games are included in the book, each carefully designed so that the components required are those found in the majority of schools or, alternatively, are easy to make.

The intention of *The Maths Collection* is to provide interesting and exciting activities for the children, a valuable support for the busy teacher, and an approach that brings mathematics to life through display and enthusiastic participation.

Kathie Barrs and Paul Briten

Place Value

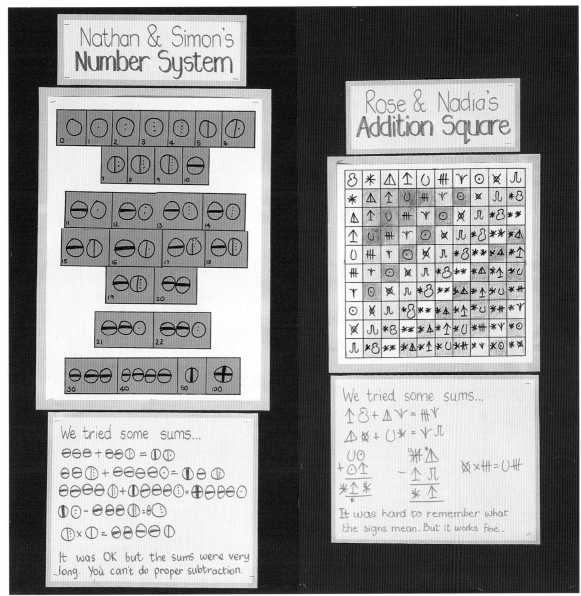

Devise your own number system

Discussion
Study different arrangements of the same digits, for example 13 and 31. What does each digit represent? What is the importance of zero in place value? What could be the implications of omitting or increasing the number of zeros (when counting money, for example)?

Items for Display
Packaging showing how objects are grouped: for example, egg boxes, cake trays, chocolate bars, 'vases' with paper flowers to be arranged in them, sets of plastic farm animals and fences, plastic money and purses, etc. Structural base apparatus such as Dienes.

Activities, Ideas and Investigations
● Devise games in different bases which give practice in grouping and exchanging. When using dice in such games, the dice need to be numbered accordingly -
    Base 3 - 1,2,1,2,1,2
    Base 4 - 1,2,3,1,2,3
    Base 5 - 1,2,3,3,4,4....etc.
(Omitting zero eliminates the need to miss a go occasionally.)

- Play games with Dienes apparatus.

  Build a Cube (3 base). Use a die, and collect the number of units shown on the die. When you have three units, exchange for a long . When you have three longs, exchange for a flat. Three flats make a cube - you win!

  Build a Castle (4 base). Play as for the previous game until the 'keep' is made from a 4x4 cube. Now build four towers from four longs, and four turrets from four units.

  Build a Square (10 base). Play as before. The aim is to make a 10x10 flat square.

  Lose a hundred (10 base). Start with a 10x10 flat and remove units by decomposing.

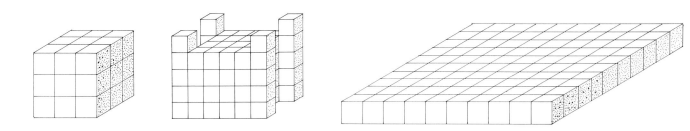

- Play 'Boxes'. Use cards numbered 0-9 placed face down. Each player has a grid, and takes a turn to take one of the cards, which are placed on the grid to make the largest number possible. The one who manages to finish with the largest number wins that game. Try varying the rules: for example, have two boards each, and add the combined numbers to obtain a score at the end.

- In teams of no more than ten, play People Numbers. Give each team a set of identical cards, enough for one per child (0-5 if 6 in the team, 0-9 if 10 in the team, etc). The 'caller' calls out a number made from 2/3/4 digits, for example 'Three thousand four hundred and seventy one'. The winning team is the first to organise its members who are holding the relevant cards into the right order to show that number.

- How would spiders count? What about donkeys, or beetles?

- Use an abacus board to reinforce place value principles. Position counters to represent a number, for example 26, on the board. Then move them two places to the left, and read off the number that is shown now, i.e. 2600.

th	h	t	u
		O	OOO
		O	OOO
		2	6

th	h	t	u
OO	OO		
O	OOO		
2	6	O	O

- Using five counters on a tens and units abacus board, how many different numbers can be shown? Extend the activity by changing the number of counters.

- Research number systems from other civilisations, for example, Egyptian, Roman, Sumerian, Gujarati, Hindu, Mayan. How do other systems record large numbers?

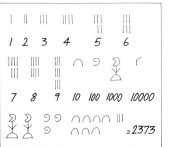

- Devise your own number systems. **(SEE PHOTOGRAPH)**

- Leading on from experience of games in different bases, try addition in different bases, using base boards. Progress to recording on an abacus, using coloured beads and a pre-arranged scheme. For example, three red beads on the right rod can be exchanged for one green bead on the middle rod, and three greens can be exchanged for one purple bead on the left rod. Practise counting on and counting back (using decomposition).

Four rules

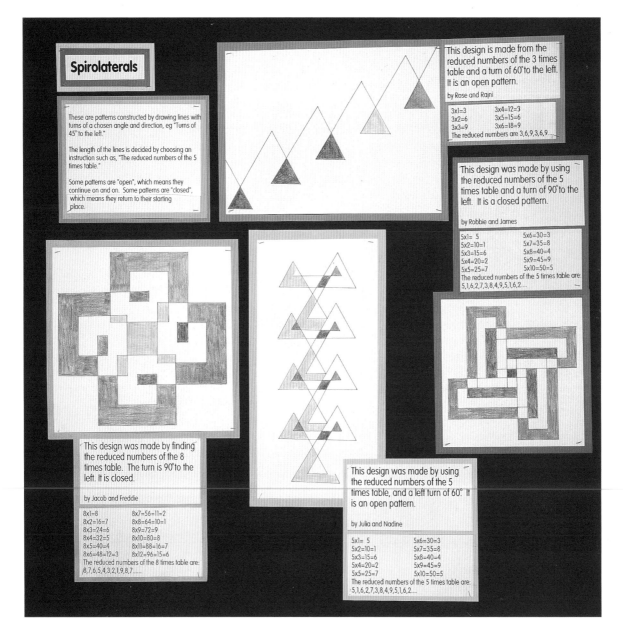

Spirolaterals

These are patterns constructed by drawing lines with turns of a chosen angle and direction, eg "Turns of 45° to the left."

The length of the lines is decided by choosing an instruction such as, "The reduced numbers of the 5 times table."

Some patterns are "open", which means they continue on and on. Some patterns are "closed", which means they return to their starting place.

This design is made from the reduced numbers of the 3 times table and a turn of 60° to the left. It is an open pattern.

by Rose and Rajni

3x1=3 3x4=12=3
3x2=6 3x5=15=6
3x3=9 3x6=18=9
The reduced numbers are 3,6,9,3,6,9...

This design was made by using the reduced numbers of the 5 times table and a turn of 90° to the left. It is a closed pattern.

by Robbie and James

5x1= 5 5x6=30=3
5x2=10=1 5x7=35=8
5x3=15=6 5x8=40=4
5x4=20=2 5x9=45=9
5x5=25=7 5x10=50=5
The reduced numbers of the 5 times table are:
5,1,6,2,7,3,8,4,9,5,1,6,2....

This design was made by finding the reduced numbers of the 8 times table. The turn is 90° to the left. It is closed.

by Jacob and Freddie

8x1=8   8x7=56=11=2
8x2=16=7 8x8=64=10=1
8x3=24=6 8x9=72=9
8x4=32=5 8x10=80=8
8x5=40=4 8x11=88=16=7
8x6=48=12=3 8x12=96=15=6
The reduced numbers of the 8 times table are:
8,7,6,5,4,3,2,1,9,8,7......

This design was made by using the reduced numbers of the 5 times table, and a left turn of 60°. It is an open pattern.

by Julia and Nadine

5x1= 5 5x6=30=3
5x2=10=1 5x7=35=8
5x3=15=6 5x8=40=4
5x4=20=2 5x9=45=9
5x5=25=7 5x10=50=5
The reduced numbers of the 5 times table are:
5,1,6,2,7,3,8,4,9,5,1,6,2....

Discussion

Why do we need to add, subtract, multiply and divide? Think of other words we use for these operations - for example, plus, minus, times. Which machines can help us to work out answers to number problems? If we have machines, why do we need to learn how to add, subtract, etc? Name some games and sports in which numbers are important.

Items for Display

Calculators, abacuses, Napier's Bones, slide rule, 100 square with number tables, addition grids, multiplication grids.

Activities, Ideas and Investigations

● Follow a trail leading to a hidden treasure.

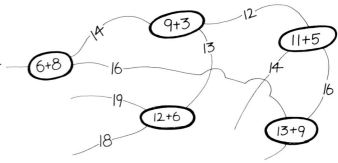

● Make a target for rolling marbles. Add scores together to work out the total.

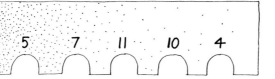

● Investigate magic squares.

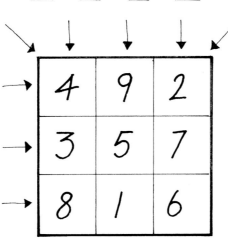

● Create new magic squares.
● When completed, add together the numbers in the inside square.

8		
	9	
12		10

13			1
2	11	7	14
3		6	15

● Learn to subtract quickly by using stepping stones.

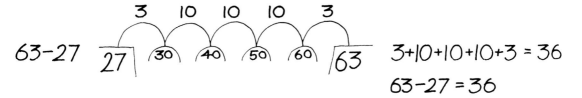

$63-27$

$3+10+10+10+3 = 36$

$63-27 = 36$

● Count on in threes and shade the numbers reached on a hundred square. Form other patterns on hundred squares by counting on using different numbers. Link patterns on hundred squares to multiplication.

● Use number lines to link addition and multiplication

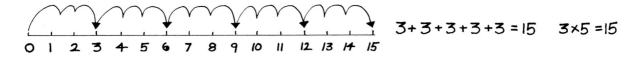

$3+3+3+3+3 = 15$ $3 \times 5 = 15$

and to link subtraction and division. How many groups of four can be made from 12?

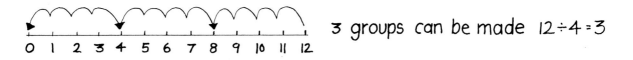

3 groups can be made $12 \div 4 = 3$

8

● Investigate number trios, e.g. 6+8=14; 8+6=14; 14-8=6; 14-6=8

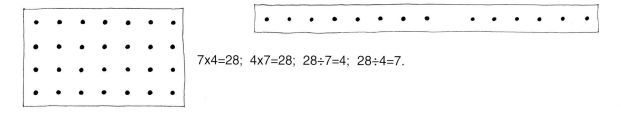

7x4=28; 4x7=28; 28÷7=4; 28÷4=7.

● Construct some interesting number machines.

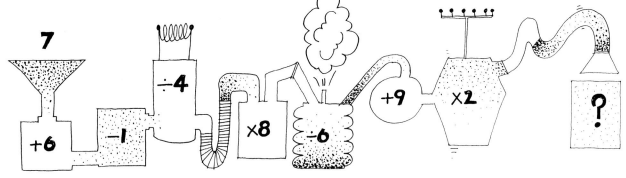

● Use digital sums (reduced numbers) to check addition and multiplication problems, for example,

```
    6 1 2  →  6+1+2 =9
 ×    1 5  →    1+5 =6  ×
  3 0 6 0             ‾54‾   5+4 =⑨
  6 1 2 0
  ‾9 1 8 0‾  →  9+1+8+0= 18   1+8 =⑨
```

```
   31      3+1 = 4
+  26      2+6 = 8  +
  ‾57‾          ‾12‾
  5+7 = 12     1+2 =③
  1 + 2 =③
```

● Discover patterns in Pascal's triangle, for example: study diagonal lines; add the numbers in each row; shade boxes containing even numbers; shade boxes containing sets of multiples; add together the numbers along any diagonal line, starting at the end of the triangle. Locate this sum on the next diagonal line. Repeat with different lines and find a pattern.

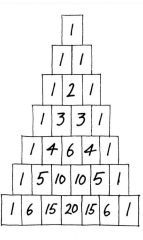

● Complete targets for the four operations.

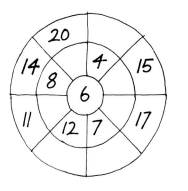
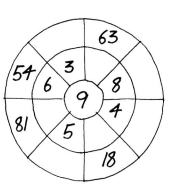

9

● Press a limited number of keys on a calculator no more than once each to generate a number. How many different numbers can you generate in this way? For example, using only the keys:

● What is the largest number you can produce by pressing specified keys only once? For example, using only the keys:

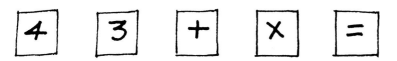

● Estimate answers to number problems and check their accuracy on a calculator.

● Try to produce given numbers using only certain keys. For example, try to produce the number 58, using the keys:

● Enter the number 6384 on a calculator. Replace the 3 with a 0 without changing the other figures.

● Make up a set of Napier's Bones.

● Investigate spirolaterals, which are patterns made from lines of different lengths turning at a constant angle. The lengths of the lines are determined by sets of numbers such as the digital sums of the multiplication tables. **(SEE PHOTOGRAPH)**

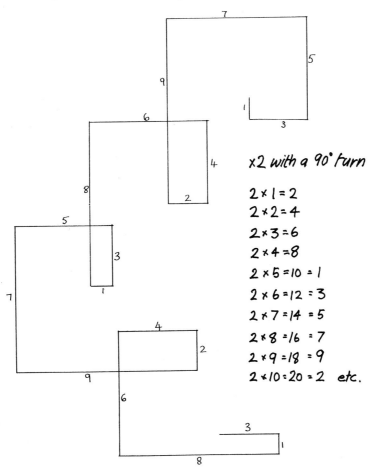

x2 with a 90° turn

2 × 1 = 2
2 × 2 = 4
2 × 3 = 6
2 × 4 = 8
2 × 5 = 10 = 1
2 × 6 = 12 = 3
2 × 7 = 14 = 5
2 × 8 = 16 = 7
2 × 9 = 18 = 9
2 × 10 = 20 = 2   etc.

Factors, Products and Prime Numbers

Discussion

If the class is to be split into groups with an equal number in each group, what are the possible numbers of groups? Are there numbers of children that would make splitting into equal groups impossible? When packing boxes of cakes, why is it easier to pack boxes of six or eight rather than boxes of five or seven?

Items for Display

A '100 square' with counters, a multiplication square, a pack of large counters for forming patterns.

Activities, Ideas and Investigations

3x5=15   5x3=15   **15 is the product of 5 and 3.**
3x4=12   4x3=12   **3 and 4 are factors of 12.**
2x6=12   6x2=12   1x12=12   12x1=12   **1, 2, 6 and 12 are also factors of 12.**

● Design or make a product machine and a factor machine. **(SEE PHOTOGRAPH)**

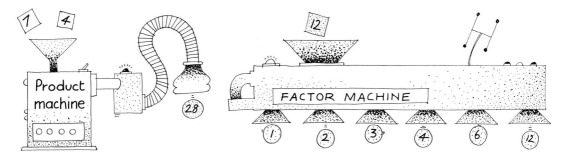

● Write down the factors of all numbers up to 20. Work out how many factors each number has.

● Find numbers which can be shown by using a square pattern of dots, for example,

16

Make a list of these SQUARE NUMBERS. Do they have an odd or even number of factors? Find some numbers greater than 20 which are square numbers. Do all square numbers have an odd number of factors?

● 12 is a RECTANGULAR NUMBER. List all of the other rectangular numbers up to 24.

● Construct a multiplication square on squared paper. Shade in all of the square numbers. Can you discover a symmetrical pattern?

7	8	9	10
14	16	18	20
21	24	27	30
28	32	36	40

● Outline some rectangles and squares on a multiplication square. Investigate the link between the products of numbers in opposite corners.
28x10= ?   40x7= ?

17	16	15	14	13
18	5	4	3	12
↓	6	1	2	11
↓	7	8	9	10
→ → →				

● Draw a number spiral on squared paper. Shade in all the square numbers. Find a pattern.

● List any numbers up to 20 that have only two factors, the number itself and the number one. These numbers are called PRIME NUMBERS. Find all prime numbers up to 100 using the Sieve of Eratosthenes. On the hundred square, shade the number one. It has only one factor and is not a prime number. Then shade all the multiples of 2, except 2 itself. Shade all the multiples of 3, except 3 itself. Shade all the multiples of 5, except 5 itself. Finally, shade all the multiples of 7, except 7 itself. The numbers that are not shaded are all the prime numbers up to 100.

● What is the largest prime number you can find?

● $2^2=2x2=4$ **4 has 3 factors** $2^3=2x2x2=8$ **8 has 4 factors**
$2^4=2x2x2x2=16$ **16 has 5 factors**   Does this pattern continue?

● Consider Goldbach's Theory: Every even number larger than 6 is the sum of two odd primes.
Every odd number larger than 7 is the sum of three odd primes.

● Start with 12 counters. Two players take turns to throw a dice. If a player can add or subtract the number of counters shown on the dice to form a prime number, a point is scored. If a player claims a prime number and the opponent can place the counters to form a rectangle or square, the opponent gains a point. At each throw a player must add or subtract the number of counters shown by the dice whether or not a prime number can be formed. The winner is the first player to score five points.

● For many years before powerful computers, the largest prime number discovered was 2^{2281} -1. Can you work out this number? (Currently, the largest prime number discovered has 65,087 digits.)

● Investigate prime factors.

● A perfect number is equal to the sum of all its factors (for example, the number 6). Can you discover any more perfect numbers?

Money

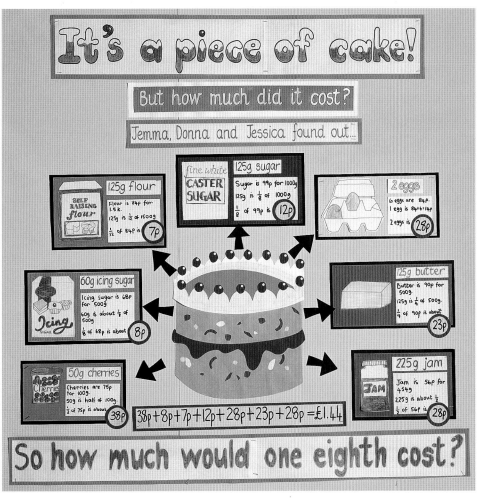

Discussion

Why do we need money? How would we manage without money? Is everything that we consider precious worth a lot of money? Is there anything that money can't buy? Do the children have pocket money? Do they spend it all, or save some? Does anyone have to work for their money? Is a bartering system a good idea? (There is a countrywide bartering system in Britain based on a 'currency' known as Links.) Where does your pocket money come from? See how far it can be traced back - parent, bank, employer, etc. Talk about Imperial and Metric coinage.

Items for Display

Currency from this and other countries, together with currency conversion charts. Sample cheque books, paying-in books, etc. Purses and wallets. Set up a shop, bank or post office in the classroom.

Activities, Ideas and Investigations

● Have a day when the children get paid in buttons for working, helping, tidying up, etc. By the end of the day they will have an unmanageable amount of buttons. How can we ease the problem of bulk? Should the bigger/metal/pretty ones be worth more?

● On a hundred square, allow one small square to represent 1p, and therefore one strip = 10p. Ask the children to colour given amounts, or interpret the amounts shown on the square. This can also be done using Cuisenaire apparatus.

● Can the children devise a 'ready reckoner' to convert one currency to another (for example, pounds to French francs)?

● Make a table to show different ways to pay for an item. Work out the fewest possible coins (or notes) to pay for different items.

How can you pay for it?
Pencil case £1·35

£1	50p	20p	10p	5p	2p	1p
✓		✓	✓	✓		
	✓✓		✓✓✓	✓		
✓		✓		✓✓	✓✓	✓

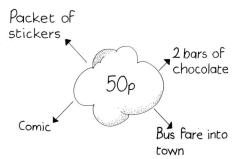

Packet of stickers

50p

2 bars of chocolate

Comic

Bus fare into town

- Discuss the purchasing power of notes and coins.

- Calculate the approximate amount your family spends on, for example, biscuits per year. Use historical records from the local library or museum to research family budgets in the past.

- Visit a local shop to research the prices of a range of items. Devise a table with gaps to be completed.

Item	Cost	Change from £1	Cost for 3
Baked beans	46p		
Sugar		2/p	
Bread			£1.17

- Count money by sorting into types of coins, and then into piles of given amounts. Design a money-sorting machine.
- Cost real events. Organise and run a 'tuck shop' at school for a month, purchasing stock and keeping income and expenditure accounts.
- Consider the 'shopkeeper's method' for giving change.
- Discuss simple economics. How many people are involved in getting an item on to the shelf in a shop? How much of the selling price goes to each individual involved? If a toy car costs £2.50, and the retailers get 30% of the selling price, how much do they actually receive when they sell one car?
- Calculate the cost of baking a birthday cake **(SEE PHOTOGRAPH)**, or making a buggy (in Technology).
- Plan a party for either younger children or parents. Estimate amounts of food, find out prices from several retail outlets, and calculate the cost per head.
- Practise rounding up and down to add up a long shopping till receipt.
- Find three items which cost approximately the same amount in a catalogue. Consider which gives the best value, and why. Would everyone agree with you?
- Buy three packs of biscuits and find the cost of an individual biscuit from each pack. Which do you consider to be best value, and why?

- Compare the prices at a local shop with those at a large supermarket. Discuss the reasons for the differences, and the advantages and disadvantages of each. Is it cheaper to buy in bulk?

local shop		Supermarket	
Advantage	Disadvantage	Advantage	Disadvantages
Friendly. Local.	Expensive. Not as much fresh food.	Fresh food. Lots of choice.	Further away. Not so personal.

- Create a data base of prices of basic foodstuffs. Budget for several different imaginary families living in an imaginary street, for example, a single mother and toddler, a senior citizen living alone, a family of six, a young couple, etc. Take into account the need to have a healthy diet.
- Plan a residential school trip. Sort the class into groups, each having responsibility for costing one aspect such as accommodation, travel arrangements, catering and activities. Provide timetables, maps, menus, etc. Conduct surveys into the likes and dislikes of classmates, and come up with sample costings for several different types of trips.
- Use travel brochures to find the cost of various types of holidays.
- Write stories about: something very small but very expensive; something very large but not worth very much; something so precious you can't buy it.
- Play Monopoly, and devise a version based on local places.

Fractions and Decimals

Discussion

Why do we need to use fractions? Discuss 'fair shares'. Why do we need decimals as well as fractions? Give examples of occasions when decimals are used. In which sports are fractions and decimals important?

Items for Display

Abacus, calculator, counters, 10x10 square grids, clock face, shapes illustrating different fractions, fraction dominoes, decimal dominoes.

Activities, Ideas and Investigations

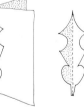

- Draw shapes and divide them into halves and quarters.

- Make a bookmark by folding a piece of paper in half and cutting out a shape.

- Draw clock faces to illustrate *half past*, *quarter past* and *quarter to* times.
- Make some interesting shapes by folding a piece of paper into quarters and cutting out a shape (at the folded corner).
- Draw diagrams to illustrate these fractions: $1/3$, $1/5$, $1/6$, $1/8$, $1/10$.
- Draw five 4x3 rectangles on squared paper. Shade different fractions of these rectangles, for example, $3/4$, $7/12$, $11/12$, $5/6$, $2/3$. Write the five fractions in order of size, starting with the smallest.
- How many different ways can you find to shade: half a square, a quarter of a square?
- How many counters are there in half of a group of 24? Division will help....24 ÷2 = ? Use counters and division to find other fractions of the group, for example,1) $1/4$, 2) $1/3$, 3) $1/6$, 4) $1/12$, 5) $2/3$, 6) $3/4$, 7) $5/6$, 8) $7/12$.
- Can six children have a fair share of ten cakes? What can be done to solve the problem?

- Draw diagrams to illustrate equivalent fractions.

I Whole		
$1/3$	$1/3$	$1/3$

$1/6$	$1/6$	$1/6$	$1/6$	$1/6$	$1/6$

I Whole				
$1/5$	$1/5$	$1/5$	$1/5$	$1/5$

$1/10$	$1/10$	$1/10$	$1/10$	$1/10$	$1/10$	$1/10$	$1/10$	$1/10$	$1/10$

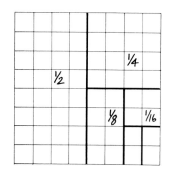

● Divide a square as many times as possible by halving the remaining space.

● Use a grid to illustrate as many different fractions as possible, for example,

$\frac{2}{10}$

● Divide a rectangle into tenths to link decimals and fractions.

One tenth or nought point one (0·1) of the rectangle is shaded.

● Illustrate other decimal fractions:

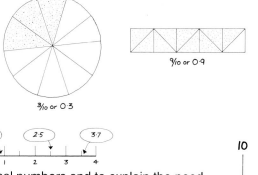

9/10 or 0·9

3/10 or 0·3

● Link decimals to a number line:

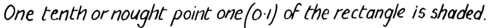

● Use an abacus to illustrate decimal numbers and to explain the need for a decimal point.

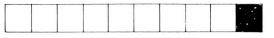

T   u   t   T   u   t

10   1   ¹/₁₀

3   1 · 4

● Multiply and divide by ten:

0 · 6 × 10 =   6 · 0

● Link decimals to money: £2·64 ⟶ £$\frac{4}{100}$ or 4p

£2 ⟶ £$\frac{6}{10}$ or 60p

● Use a calculator to change fractions to decimals, for example,

$^1/_2$ $1 \div 2 = 0.5$
$^3/_4$ $3 \div 4 = 0.75$

● Consider decimal places beyond hundredths using an abacus.
● Use mixed numbers, e.g. $^3/_5 + ^7/_{10} = ^6/_{10} + ^7/_{10} = ^{13}/_{10}$ or $1\ ^3/_{10}$.
● Cut strips from a multiplication square to investigate equivalent fractions. Use the square to write different fractions with the same denominator, for example, for $^1/_5$ and $^5/_6$. Find the smallest number that occurs on both the 5 line and the 6 line. This number is 30. Using this number as the new denominator $^1/_5 = ^6/_{30}$ and $^5/_6 = ^{25}/_{30}$
● Make a list of measuring devices that use fractions or decimals.
● Find out about the Italian mathematician Fibonacci, and the Fibonacci sequence.
● Find out about the 'golden fraction'. **(SEE PAGE 22)**
● Investigate recurring decimals.
● Draw pictures using a fraction of a 100 square. **(SEE PHOTOGRAPH)**

Algebra

Discussion

'If the answer is 12, what could the question be?' 'If the answer is purple, what could the question be?' 'If the answer is two right-angled triangles, what could the question be?' Is there only one answer to these problems? How many ways can the children find to direct someone to the door of the classroom? For example, 'Take three steps forward, turn right, take four steps forward....'

Items for Display

Calculator, coloured counters, 100 square, paper or fabric with repeating patterns.

Activities, Ideas and Investigations

● Link multiplication and division. If 5x6=30; 6x ☐ =30; 30 ÷ ☐ =6; 30 ÷ ☐ =5

● Using an addition wall with three bricks along the bottom row, investigate the effect of changing the order of the numbers, for example, 258 or 285 or 582 or 528 or 825 or 852. Which order gives the highest total on the top brick? Now try with four numbers on the first row, and then six. Can you find a formula? To help, try replacing the numbers with letters.

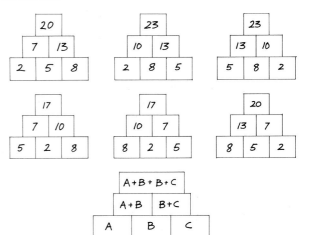

To get the largest possible number on the top, put the largest number on the central brick at the bottom.

17

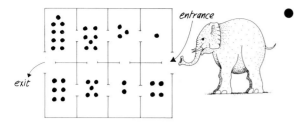

● Play 'The Elephant and the Buns'. Start with a plan of a series of rooms, each with a different number of buns in them (use Smarties, or other small sweets). Investigate problems such as: Which route would the elephant take if he were in a hurry? How many buns would he eat on the way? If the elephant were only allowed to eat an even number of buns, which routes could he take? What is the largest number of buns he could eat while passing through the house? What is the least number?

● Investigate triangular numbers and square numbers. For example, 1 triangle needs 3 matchsticks, 2 triangles need 5 matchsticks, etc.

● Play 'What's my number?' on a 100 square. 'Is it in the same row as the number 26?' etc.
● Work on magic squares.
● Play 'Last One Out'. Play with a partner, and take turns to remove either 1, 2 or 3 matchsticks from a pile of eleven. The one who takes the last one is the loser.
● Find routes for a frog to cross a lily pond, landing on the leaves which have numbers on them. Give conditions such as 'You can only land on leaves with even numbers on them'.
● Design sets of dominoes using number facts instead of dots. The following could all be joined together - 12, 3x4, 6x2, 24 ÷ 2, etc.
● Follow a simple knitting or weaving pattern.
● Play Multiplication Jigsaws - re-assemble a cut-up multiplication square. Extend this by mixing two different squares together.
● Using inverse operations, make up puzzles - along the lines of 'Think of a Number'. For example, 'Think of a number (6). Double it (12). Subtract 2 (10). Halve it (5). Add 1 (6 - the original number). Take away the number you first thought of (0). Add 10(10). Halve it (5). You have ended up with number 5.'

● Devise an addition table using symbols rather than numbers. Ask the children to complete it and to devise their own.

● Play 'Make my number', where a selection of five numbers are used to make a sixth number. You may use any of four operations ÷ - x and +, but you may not use any of the five original numbers more than once.

$9 \times 4 - 2 = 34$

● Investigate reduced numbers (digital sums) which are found when the digits of a number are added together until a single digit is reached. For example, the reduced number of 78 is 6 (7+8=15, 1+5=6).
Show reduced numbers on circles divided into 8, 9 or 10 points.
Find the patterns in reduced consecutive numbers, even numbers, odd numbers, etc.
Reduce the numbers on a multiplication square and study the patterns.

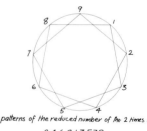

patterns of the reduced number of the 2 times table.
2 4 6 8 1 3 5 7 9

● Find out about the work of Fibonacci and Pascal. Generate sequences yourselves (for example, 'Double the previous number and subtract one') and see if you can solve each other's sequence.
Following investigations into the Fibonacci sequence (where each number in a sequence is the sum of the two preceding numbers), draw a line of six squares and fill in the missing numbers when only the first and last have been given.
You can find the sum of any ten consecutive numbers in a Fibonacci sequence by multiplying the seventh number in that group by 11. For example, 9,2,11,13,24,37,61,98,159,257 = 671, and 61x11=671)
● Design wrapping paper using a repeating pattern.
● Explore repeating patterns in music - *ostinato*.
● Find the perimeter of a square given only the length of one side.
● Consider formulae – to convert °F to °C. F-32 = $9/5$ C
    – for finding perimeter and area of a circle.
● Try to obtain palindromic numbers (which read the same backwards as forwards, for example, 4224), by adding together two numbers, the second being the reverse of the first. For example:

1 stage	2 stage	3 stage
125	85	746
+ 521	+ 58	+ 647
646	143	1393
	+ 341	+ 3931
	484	5324
		+ 4235
		9559

Time

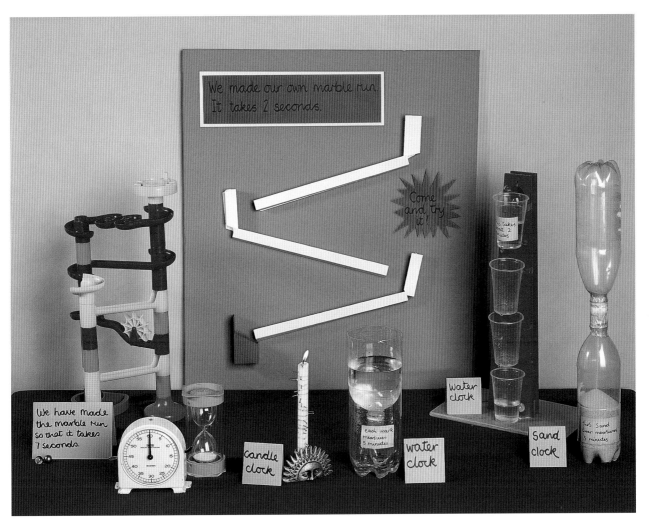

Discussion

What instruments do we use to tell the time? When do we need to tell the time accurately, or approximately? Can we measure periods of time without a mechanical instrument? Do we control time or are we its slave? What would happen if time had to be metricated?

Items for Display

A variety of analogue and digital clocks and watches - working or beyond repair. Devices for measuring periods of time - homemade and commercially produced, for example, egg-timers, sand and water clocks, stop watch. Timetables for train, bus and plane. Radio and television programme schedules, calendars, diaries, class timetable. Geared demonstration clock with moving hands.

Activities, Ideas and Investigations

● Draw clock faces, linking with pictures of the day's events.

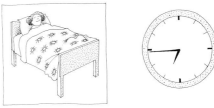

● Complete and learn the poem for the months of the year - 'Thirty days has September'.

● Here is part of a calendar for the year 3000. Work out for the year 3000 on which day of the week the following days will fall: a) New Year's Day b) 29th February c) your birthday d) Christmas Day.

MARCH				
Su	5	12	19	26
M	6	13	20	27
Tu	7	14	21	28
W	1	8	15	22	29
Th	2	9	16	23	30
F	3	10	17	24	31
Sa	4	11	18	25

- Try to find number patterns on a calendar.
- Design some unusual clocks and watches.
- Estimate the passing of one minute. Work out the difference in seconds between the estimate and 60 seconds.
- Work out activities that you think will take one minute, two minutes, five minutes, half an hour, etc. Carry out the activities and time them. Work out the difference between each time and the estimate.
- Consider daily activities, for example, time taken cleaning teeth, eating, watching television, sleeping. How long would be spent on these activities during a month or a year?
- Study sundials, shadow clocks, sand and water clocks, candle clocks, pendulums. Design a timer to record a certain interval of time, for example, 10 seconds, one minute. **(SEE PHOTOGRAPH)**
- Design and make a marble run. **(SEE PHOTOGRAPH)**
- How could you measure the passage of time if you were shipwrecked on a desert island?
- Estimate and then time events to the nearest second using a stopwatch or stop clock; for example, walking 100m, or reading a page of a book. Record times for different people and display the results as a graph.

- Consider different types of timetable - school timetable, rail, bus and airport timetables, radio and television schedules. Create your ideal television timetable for a day. Consider the importance of a.m. and p.m. and consider the benefits of the 24 hour clock.

- Construct timelines for a school day, a week, a century of inventions.

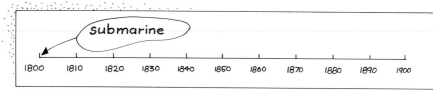

- Draw a graph to show the pulse rate of four different people. Record each person's pulse rate after one minute's exercise. Can you use your pulse to help estimate a period of one minute?
- Measure personal speed in metres per second. Consider cycle and car speeds in km/h. Work out average speeds from journey graphs.

- Estimate the time when a clock minute hand is missing.

- Investigate pendulums of varying length. Does a heavier or lighter weight affect the swing of a pendulum?

- Make up a set of time dominoes.

Length

These are the paper patterns we used to make the waistcoat.

And it fits!

Discussion

How many units can you think of for measuring length? Why/when do we need to measure length?
Is there a need for standard measures, and why? Research standard and non-standard measures from other cultures and times - in particular, body measurements such as cubits. Is estimation important, and if so, why? How do we decide which unit of measurement to use?

Items for Display

Measuring implements, such as tape measures, trundle wheels, map measuring gadgets, calipers, rulers.
Maps. Conversion charts from imperial to metric measures. Distance charts in miles or kilometres.

Activities, Ideas and Investigations

● Practise measuring in the environment, firstly by using metre sticks and trundle wheels. Then measure to the nearest half and quarter metre by marking these on the metre ruler. Next, use decimetre strips (10cm long), and measure to the nearest 10cm. Introduce centimetre measures when there is a need for more accuracy. Finally, use millimetres for very accurate measuring.
● Ask the children to order themselves by height, arm span, head circumference, etc.

● Collect body measurements such as wrist, ankle, waist, chest, arm and hand span, etc., in order to investigate relationships. For example, arm span is often the same as the height of the child. What measurement is approximately the same as the circumference of the head? Are the relationships between the measurements of a child's body the same as those of an adult? Does the tallest person also have the longest hand span/largest feet, etc?

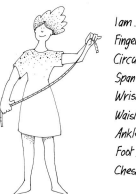

I am _____ cm tall
Finger tip to finger tip _____ cm
Circumference of head ____ cm
Span _____ cm
Wrist ____ cm
Waist ____ cm
Ankle ____ cm
Foot _____ cm
Chest _____ cm

- Challenge the children to design and make a hat for their friend - which fits! Hold a fashion show.
- Relate the skill of measuring to aspects of Science, for example, growth. Measure and record the long-term growth of newly planted trees (their trunk circumference, canopy, height and the length of a selected branch), or (for short-term) measure and record the growth of cress.
- Make 2D or 3D maps and use them to:

    Find distances between places - how do we measure a winding road?

    Find the shortest routes between places.

    Find routes which fulfil given criteria, for example, 'I have to pick the children up on the way'.
- Extend this by relating it to driving a car - 'How much would it cost to drive from A to B, if a car does seven miles to the litre, and petrol costs 48p a litre?'
- Using a map of the school, find distances between different rooms. Try to estimate how far you walk on an average school day. What about during playtimes?
- Sports Days are ideal opportunities to use measuring skills. Measure and mark out the race tracks. Make a measuring strip for the long jump, standing jump and 'high touch', where the children jump up and use wet fingers or chalk to make a mark on the wall. Include research into whether height and length of leg or arm has any effect on results, and if so, in which events?
- Using cardboard, design and make a 'Tidy Box' for the tables in the classroom, to include a place to store pens, pencils, rulers, rubbers, etc. Cover it in decorative paper, using the smallest possible piece.
- Research the size of a chosen dinosaur and mark it out on the playground.
- See who can make the longest piece of paper from an A4 sheet.

- Look at different ways of converting kilometres to miles:
    - Divide by 8 and multiply by 5.
    - Round up or down to nearest 10, take off the zero and multiply by six. (This method is a rough guide.)
    - By using the Fibonacci sequence (see page 18).

165 KILOMETRES = 102 MILES (APPROX)

3, 6, 9, 15, 24, 39, 63, 102, 165

39 KILOMETRES = 24 MILES (APPROX)

1, 5, 6, 11, 17, 28, 45

28 KM = 17 MILES (APPROX)

- Using a thick book, find a way to measure the thickness of one page.
- Study Leonardo's drawing of a man in a circle, which is a study in proportion. Practise drawing human figures using the correct proportions. For example, the height of an adult male is approximately $7\frac{1}{2}$ times the size of the head. Look at the proportions of the human head when drawing. For example, the eyes are about halfway down the head.
- Find out about measurement of depth for ships (fathoms) and altitude for aeroplanes.
- Investigate perimeters - including perimeters of coins.

- Research the Golden Section, which is a theory relating to the division of space into proportions which are pleasing to the human eye.

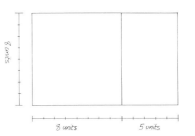

- Using a World Atlas, find distances between capital cities of the world or holiday destinations. Set the children challenges such as 'I want to go on holiday somewhere warm, but I don't want to travel further than 400 miles. Where could I go?'
- Practise writing measurements in different forms, for example, 836mm/83.6cm/0.836m. Make snap games based on this.
- Using a paper pattern made from measuring the body, make a simple item of clothing such as a waistcoat or skirt. More simply, make a fabric case from a pattern, for an item such as a recorder, or a dust jacket for a book. **(SEE PHOTOGRAPH)**
- Calculate the number of rolls of wallpaper needed to decorate someone's bedroom.
- Look at Ordnance Survey maps to see how height above sea level is shown on maps (contours).
- Find out about unusual measurements from the Guinness Book of Records.

Capacity

Discussion
When is it important to know how much liquid a container will hold? When do we need to measure quantities of liquid? What units are commonly used when measuring capacity?

Items for Display
A range of containers of different sizes. One litre measure. Measures for 500ml, 250ml, 100ml, 50ml and 10ml. Empty bottles and cartons showing capacities, medicine spoon, egg cup, plastic funnel.

Activities, Ideas and Investigations
● Compare the capacities of pairs of containers by filling one with water, sand or rice, and emptying the contents into the second container. Use this method to work out which of four containers has 1) the largest capacity, 2) the smallest capacity.

● Use three other containers. Find out which has the largest capacity by seeing how many eggcups full of water you need to fill each container.
● Roll an A4 piece of paper into a cylinder lengthways. Glue, and fill with a substance such as rice or sand. Repeat with another sheet rolled widthways. Which holds more?
● Establish the benefit of a standard measure. Introduce the litre measure.

● Find containers that hold 1) more than one litre, 2) less than one litre, 3) about the same as one litre.
● Which holds more, a pint bottle or a litre carton of milk?

● Study larger containers. Estimate how many litres of water they will hold, then measure.
● Estimate how many eggcups could be filled using one litre of water, then measure.

- Use a litre measure to find the approximate capacity of 1) a bucket, 2) a bowl, 3) a large ice cream carton.
- Establish the need for a unit of measure smaller than the litre.

- Show 1 litre = 1000 millilitres. Estimate the capacity of 10 different containers. Measure their capacity as accurately as possible using a graduated measure. Work out the difference between each estimate and measure, and display the results in a table.

CONTAINER	ESTIMATE	MEASURE	DIFFERENCE
	ml	ml	ml
	ml	ml	ml
	ml	ml	ml
	ml	ml	ml

- Find out how much water you can hold in your hands. Compare with your friends. Do the largest hands hold the most water?
- Calculate the amount of drink needed for a party. Allow two plastic cups full per person.
- Use a 5ml medicine spoon to find the approximate capacities of some small containers.
- Calibrate a container to measure capacities to the nearest 1) 100ml, 2) 10ml.

- Study the capacities of a range of washing-up liquid containers produced by different manufacturers. Work out which product appears to give the best value for money. Repeat this investigation for a range of other products.

- Collect five containers which appear to have about the same capacity. Try to place the containers in order of capacity. Measure the capacity of each container to see if you were correct. Draw a graph showing the capacities of the five containers.

- Using a range of different shaped glasses, how can you be sure that you pour the same amount into each glass?

- Research the amount of water we use each day for activities such as washing and drinking.
  (SEE PHOTOGRAPH)

24

Volume

Can you calculate the amount of living space Dino has in his box?

Discussion

Why is the amount of space taken up by a box important to people who sell food? Which 3-dimensional shapes can fit together leaving no gaps? What happens to a full cup of tea when you put in three lumps of sugar?

Items for Display

Centimetre cubes, displacement bucket, variety of boxes.

Activities, Ideas and Investigations

● How many different cuboids can be made using 20 centimetre cubes? The amount of space taken up by each cuboid is its volume. Do all of the cuboids have the same volume?

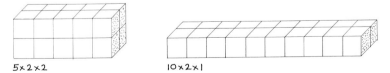

5x2x2   10x2x1

● Build two more different cuboids that have the same volume.

● Use multiplication to find out how many blocks in a cuboid: 10 cubes in each layer, and three layers, so there are 10x3, or 30 cubes in total.

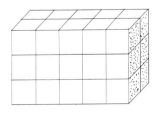

● Build other cuboids and use multiplication to work out how many blocks have been used.
● Collect a variety of food boxes. Establish the need for a standard measure to compare the amounts of space the boxes take up (i.e. the volumes).

- Volume can be measured in cubic centimetres. Build several cuboids using centimetre cubes and work out their volumes.
- Build cuboids from given dimensions. What are their volumes?

- Work out the volumes of several boxes by multiplication. For example, 2x3x6 - Volume of box = 36cm³.

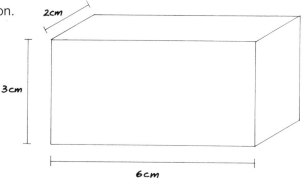

- Copy this net on to centimetre squared paper. Cut out the net, fold the paper and make a box by gluing the flaps. How many centimetre cubes are needed to fill the box? Seal the edges of the box with adhesive tape. Carefully fill the box with water. Pour the water into a measure to find out how much water the box holds. What is the capacity of the box? From the investigation you can discover that 100 cubic centimetres has the same volume as 100ml of water.

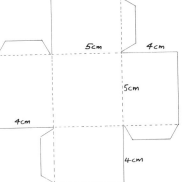

- Use thin card to make an open top box measuring 10cm x 10cm x 10cm. Glue the flaps firmly, and reinforce the seams with adhesive tape. Fill the box with water and work out the approximate amount of water contained in the box.
- Study a litre cube measure. Work out how many centimetre cubes would be needed to fill the measure. Establish that 1000 cubic centimetres have the same volume as one litre of liquid, and therefore 1ml of liquid occupies lcm³ of space. Use this knowledge to work out the capacities of other large containers by measuring the lengths of their sides.
- Make the largest possible cube or cuboid from a sheet of A3 card. Find out its volume.
- Find the volume of a cube, given only the length of an edge. Now find the length of the edge of a different cube, given only the volume.
- Using a displacement bucket, study the amount of water displaced when different objects are put into the bucket. Try to find an object that displaces about one litre of water.
- As 1ml of water occupies 1cm³ of space, use the displacement bucket to find the volumes of objects with different shapes. Try to work out a way of finding the volume of an object that does not sink, using the displacement method.

- Can you find the volume of a tennis ball?

Temperature

Discussion

When do we need to measure temperature? What units do we use for measuring temperature? Does temperature affect your choice of holiday resort? How does your body react to changes in the temperature? How is temperature measurement used in cooking? What temperature do you like the water to be when you are swimming?

Items for Display

Different types of thermometer, copies of weather forecasts, temperature readings for cities in different countries.

Activities, Ideas and Investigations

● Learn how to take temperatures using a standard room thermometer. Where should your eyes be when you are reading the thermometer? Check the temperature in different parts of the school. Check the temperature outside the school at different times during the day. Record your readings in a table.

● Where in the classroom can you find 1) the highest temperature? 2) the lowest temperature?

● Devise a table to show midday temperatures outside your school. Take the readings in the same place each time. Record your results on a vertical line graph. Compare your results with:
1) temperatures in other parts of the country
2) temperatures in other countries.

	MON	TUES	WEDS	THURS	FRI
TEMP °C (ESTIMATE)					
TEMP °C (MEASURE)					

● Draw a column graph to show the temperatures in different cities throughout the world on a particular day. Locate these cities on a globe. Is there a link between temperature and location?

● Establish that water freezes at 0°C and boils at 100°C. Where can water boil at a lower temperature? What is the normal temperature of the human body? What change in body temperature causes a person to feel ill?

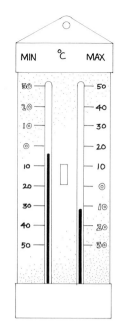

● Study a maximum/minimum thermometer. Discover how it works. Use a maximum/minimum thermometer to record maximum and minimum temperatures outside the school each day for a week. Display your results on a line graph. Be sure to record the temperatures at the same time each day. Work out the differences between each pair of maximum and minimum temperatures. Record these differences on a graph. Consider what happens when the temperature is too hot or too cold. **(SEE PHOTOGRAPH)**

● Study different temperature graphs. Write down information you can obtain from the graphs. Decide whether or not every point on a line graph has a meaning.

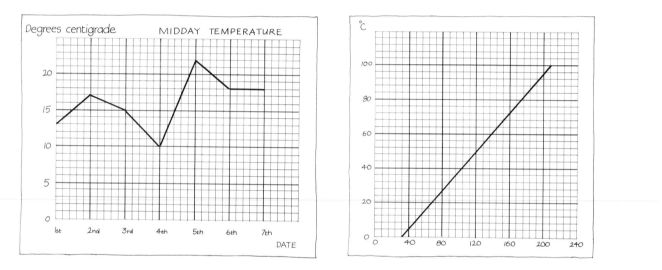

● To convert temperatures approximately from Celsius to Fahrenheit, double the temperature and add 30°. For example, 22° Celsius....22 + 22 + 30....74° Fahrenheit.
● To convert more accurately, use the equation $^9/_5 C = F-32$.

● Extend the number line to include negative numbers by considering 'minus temperatures'. Extend the line backwards on the conversion graph above to discover the Celsius temperature that is equivalent to 0° Fahrenheit.

● Investigate whether our body temperature rises when we are hot.

● Find out about reptiles.

● Carry out an investigation into the effects of insulation and heat loss.
  – Wrap identical containers in different materials and fill them with warm water. Find which container retains heat most effectively.
  – Fill different shaped containers with warm water and discover which retains heat most effectively.
  – Carry out a similar investigation using containers made of different materials, for example, pottery, metal.

● Consider the importance of energy conservation by conducting investigations around the school.
  – Measure the temperature indoors and outdoors, and discuss.
  – Measure the temperature in all the classrooms and compare. Discuss possible reasons for variations.
  – Find the warmest and coldest parts of each classroom and the rest of the school.
  – Repeat the above at different times of the day and during different weather conditions.

Weight

Maria's Pot
Before: 240g
After: 195g
Loss: 45g

Mike's
Dog & Basket
Before: 420g
After: 360g
Loss: 60g

Lynn's Mug
Before: 270g
After: 225g
Loss: 45g

Najid's Dinosaur
Before: 300g
After: 255g
Loss: 45g

Russell's Man
Before: 360g
After: 305g
Loss: 55g

Jessica's Cat
Before: 570g
After: 480g
Loss: 90g

Discussion

What makes things weigh different amounts? Do heavy things always sink in water? How can a heavy aeroplane fly? Why do things fall downwards? Discuss the need for standard measures. What would be a suitable unit of measurement to weigh a fruit gum, a shoe, etc.? How could a bus be weighed? Talk about the language used in measuring: *kilo—, milli—, gram, pound, carat, etc.* Discuss why some liquids are measured in fluid ounces and others in millilitres. Find out about early units of measurement, for example, *pecks.* Find out the correct way to lift heavy objects.

Items for Display

A selection of scales and balances, including a variety of weights. A collection of different natural materials, some of which are surprisingly light or heavy, for example, lead, feathers, pumice stone, a piece of balsa wood, a piece of hard wood. A range of food products with weight marked - include some liquids.

Activities, Ideas and Investigations

● Make three different sized Multilink animals. Order them by weight. Make three more and include them in the order. Investigate the relationship between weight and the number of cubes used.

● Using clay, make three more animals weighing different amounts. Let them dry and then reweigh them. What has happened? Did the heaviest model lose more or less weight than the lightest one? **(SEE PHOTOGRAPH)**

● Fill several identical containers with different substances - rice, sand, lentils, etc. Will the weights vary?

Do these pots all weigh the same?

- Using three objects of slightly different weights, and a pair of balances, experiment to find if the heaviest can be found allowing only two weighings. What is the minimum number of weighings to find the heaviest out of four objects? Five objects? Six objects?

- Collect packets which advertise an extra amount free, for example, 20% free. Calculate the original weight. Design and make sample packets of products, showing a certain amount free and giving the original and new weights.

- Can you find the weight of a baked bean can, without removing the contents?

- Using a range of different types of balls (ping pong, airflow, tennis, rubber, rounders, football, etc.) carry out investigations to discover the optimum weight of ball to throw the greatest distance. (If the ball is too light, it will not travel far through the air, and if it is too heavy, you will not be strong enough to throw it far.) Does each child get the best results from the same ball? What about an adult?

Food	Before cooking	After cooking	Difference
An egg			
Popcorn			
Toast			

- Carry out investigations into changes of weight before and after cooking food. Does the weight of an egg change when it is boiled? What about popcorn or rice? Does pastry lose weight when it is cooked? If so, why?

- Make bird cakes to several different recipes. Weigh them daily to discover which one is the most popular with the birds.
- After studying a range of commercially produced weights, design and make your own set of weights, either to standard measures, or to measurements of your own choice.
- Make a spring balance.
- Find out about the costs of sending parcels of different weights through the post.
- Try to work out the weight of water that can be held in a sponge.
- Cook a Victoria sandwich using the 'egg' method, where the amount of sugar, butter and flour are equivalent to the weight of the egg included in the mixture.
- Convert recipes from imperial to metric units.
- Using a recipe for, say, twelve biscuits, adapt and cook enough to make one biscuit for everyone in the class.
- Investigate ratios of fulcrums connected with see-saws. For example, if too heavy a weight is placed on one end, a balance can be achieved by either moving that object towards the central pivot, or moving the pivot itself. Stand holding a bag of sugar with one hand, close to your body. Then extend your arm and see how heavy the sugar seems now. Try carrying a heavy bucket with one hand, and watching how your other arm lifts to compensate. Why do tightrope walkers use balancing sticks?
- Find out about lifting weights using pulleys and gears.
- Research into the methods thought to have been used to construct such buildings as the pyramids or Stonehenge. Find a way to move an object which is too heavy to lift.
- Investigate whether there is a weight/value relationship with coins.
- Research into the use of ballast in ships and submarines, and the use of air tanks to control the rates of ascending and descending.
- Find out about the ways in which heavy weight is supported in architecture - flying buttresses, keystones in arches, lintels, foundations, etc.
- Find out about the effect of air pressure on the weather.

2D Shape

Discussion
What is meant by 1/2/3 dimension? (1 = a point, 2 = a line, 3 = a body). Look at shapes in the environment and also in paintings, where three dimensions are portrayed in two dimensions. Can a 3D object be changed into a 2D object? and vice versa?

Items for Display
Geoboards and elastic bands. Geostrips. MATS (Mathematical Activity Tiles) and other tessellating shapes. A set of 2D shapes.

Activities, Ideas and Investigations
● Make shadow hand puppets to investigate how light falling on an object from several positions will cast distorted shadows.
● Create patterns using a series of 2D shapes.
● In which 2D shapes will you find parallel lines?
● Investigate tessellations:
– Suggest reasons why certain shapes tessellate while others do not.
– Find which regular polygons tessellate (kitchen floor tiling patterns are useful for this).
– Make patterns using irregular shapes.
● Start with a triangle, and cut off one of the corners. What shape have you made? Try the same thing with a square, an oblong, a pentagon, etc., and record the results.

● Make a tile to tessellate by cutting out a small square of paper, perhaps 4cmx4cm. Draw a shape along one side, and cut that piece out. Pick it up, and without turning it over, place it down against the opposite side. Glue it in position, and use this tile to make a tessellating pattern.

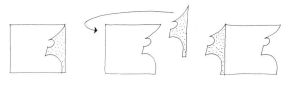

- Using Geoboards:
  - How many ways can be found to divide a geoboard into two equal sections? Investigate the relationship between the size of the geoboard and the number of ways to divide it into two.
  - Repeat, dividing it into 3/4/5 sections.
  - Find how many shapes can be made with the area of eight square units. Which has the largest/smallest perimeter? Transfer the shapes on to dotted paper.
  - Now find how many shapes can be made with a perimeter of 14 units. Investigate the areas of these shapes.
  - Using a 3x3 geoboard, explore how many different triangles can be made, not including changes in orientation or position. How many different squares or pentagons can be made?
  - Following work on classifying triangles, show these on geoboards. (You will need an isometric geoboard for an equilateral triangle.)
  - How many different sized isosceles, scalene and right-angled triangles can be made on a 4x4 geoboard? Record on dotted paper. Extend using a larger board.

- Using Geostrips:
  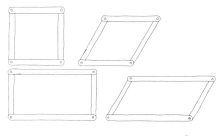
  - Make a square and change it without taking anything apart.
  - Repeat for a rectangle. What is it that has altered? Show this change on a geoboard.
  - Discuss how to make these shapes rigid (by adding struts).
  - Investigate how to make other shapes rigid, using the minimum number of struts. How many triangles are formed by adding the struts? Record, and predict how many struts would be needed to make a 50-sided shape rigid, and how many triangles would be formed in the process.

- Make different shapes and pictures using tangrams.
- Use a compass and a ruler to construct an equilateral triangle, a hexagon, a right angle, a square. Find other ways to construct 2D shapes.
- Use a 2x2 grid to find how many different arrangements of two coloured squares are possible. Try three coloured squares on a 3x3 grid, and four coloured squares on a 4x4 grid. Can you predict how many arrangements there would be for seven squares on a 7x7 grid?
- How many squares can you see in a 2x2 grid? How many in a 3x3 grid? Repeat up to a 6x6 grid. Is there a pattern? Can you predict how many can be seen in a 10x10 grid?
- Place a counter on a large plain sheet of paper, and try to explain its position to a friend who cannot see the counter. See if they can place their counter on their own sheet of paper in a similar position, by listening to your instructions.

- Make Polyominoes (which are different arrangements of squares joined by their edges), and Pentiamonds (as polyominoes but made from equilateral triangles).

2 squares = dominoes	2 triangles = diamond
3 squares = trominoes	3 triangles = triamond
4 squares = tetrominoes	4 triangles = tetriamond
5 squares = pentominoes*	5 triangles = pentiamond
6 squares = hexominoes	6 triangles = hexiamond
* (SEE PHOTOGRAPH)	**(SEE ILLUSTRATIONS ON PAGE 71)**

  How many different ways can be found to create them? Can the shapes they make be tessellated? Can the different pentominoes be arranged all together like a jigsaw, to make a rectangle? What is the perimeter of the various shapes? How many sides does each one have? Record all the above on dotted/isometric paper, and in grid form.

- Create 2D shapes using the Logo program on your computer.
- Measure the diameter of a circle with either calipers or ruler and set squares, and the circumference using a band of paper. Keep a table of results of several circles. Is there a relationship between the diameter and circumference?
- Study the work of Escher, who used tessellations in his paintings.

3D Shape

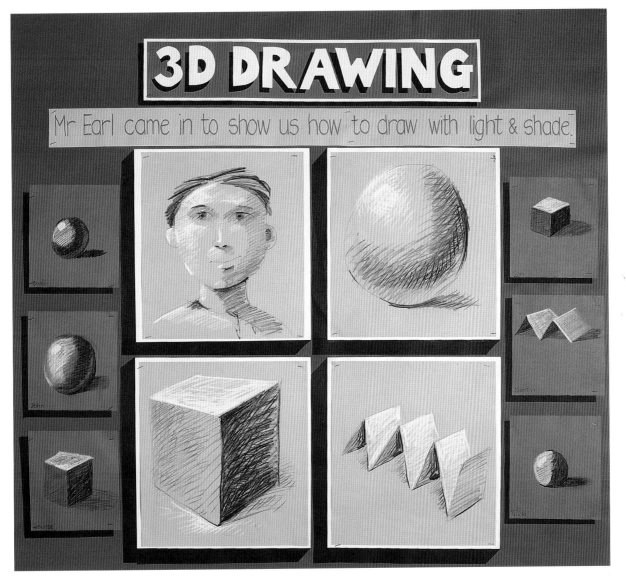

Discussion

How do we see in three dimensions? See how difficult it is to judge distances and see objects in 3D with one eye closed by trying to catch a ball with one hand. Look at some examples of packaging. Why are there no spherical packets? Look at 'Magic Eye' pictures, optical illusions, and 3D glasses. Study some pieces of sculpture as examples of 3D art forms. Provide a strong light source to one side (for example, an anglepoise light), and move it around to show the modelling more clearly. Look at the way the backgrounds to cartoons are painted on flat surfaces.

Items for Display

A collection of named solid shapes. Packaging of different shapes. Pipecleaners, straws and Plasticine. Clixi or Polydrons. MATS (Mathematical Activity Tiles). Templates of 2D shapes to make nets. **(SEE PAGE 70)**

Activities, Ideas and Investigations

● Make stacks of identical shapes to create prisms.
● Sort 3D shapes to given and chosen criteria.
● Use a Feely bag. Introduce correct terminology such as vertices and edges. Play 20 Questions - 'Which shape am I holding behind my back?'
● Which 3D shapes roll? stack? slide on an incline?

● What 3D shape is generated when a 2D shape is rotated around an axis?

33

- Unfold packets to find what shape the nets are, and use them to make new packets.
- Investigate the shapes of slices cut from 3D Plasticine shapes.
- Cover empty tins and boxes with wrapping paper to make attractive containers using the smallest amount of paper possible.
- Study bricklaying patterns and construct them with Lego.
- Design a net to make an attractive gift box. Decorate it and make something to put inside it to give as a gift.

- Look at a net, then select and draw round the correct 2D shapes to make your own identical net **(SEE PAGE 70)**. Which solid shape do you think it will make? Cut it out, score, fold and fasten with adhesive tape. (Construction skills are not important at this stage.)
    - Was the construction as predicted?
    - How many faces has it? Are they curved or straight?
    - What shape are the faces?
    - How many edges are there, and are they straight or curved?
    - Are the edges all the same length?

- Construct more complicated 3D shapes, for example, octahedron, dodecahedron, icosahedron.

- Place an equilateral triangle in the centre of a gummed paper circle and fold over the edges. Repeat four times, and glue the circles together to make a solid shape.

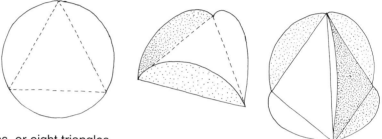

- Try with six squares, or six triangles, or eight triangles.

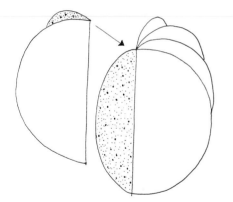

- Fold eight gummed circles in half, adhesive side out, and stick them together. What solid shapes have you made? Try with eight squares, or eight equilateral triangles.

- What happens if you fold the square diagonally?

- Make skeleton 3D shapes using straws and Plasticine, pipecleaners or thread. How many straws are needed for each shape? Are they all the same length?
- Make 3D pop-up greetings cards.
- Practise 3D drawings by using shading. (To see light and shadow, you will need a strong light source to one side.) **(SEE PHOTOGRAPH)**
- Place white 3D shapes next to a window and draw them, concentrating on using shadow to give form. **(SEE PHOTOGRAPH)**
- Fold a piece of paper into a concertina and draw, concentrating on the shadows. **(SEE PHOTOGRAPH)**
- Use a child as a model, with a strong light source (for example, anglepoise light) to one side of the model's face. Rub charcoal all over a piece of paper and use a rubber to 'draw' the highlights of the face, rather than shading in the dark areas.
- Study perspective drawing, using vanishing points and horizons. **(SEE PHOTOGRAPH PAGE 43)**
- Study Origami, where 3D shapes are created from a piece of paper.
- Make 3D shoebox theatres.
- Using clay or plaster of Paris, sculpt heads either by building up (using clay), or carving away (using plaster).

Angles and Bearings

Discussion

Consider devices that turn - door handles, car wheels, etc. Which of these devices can make a full turn? Which turn clockwise, anti-clockwise, both? How can you measure an amount of turn (dynamic concept of an angle)? Angles are formed when two lines meet (static concept of an angle). When must these angles be measured carefully? How do we measure angles? In which games do turns and angles play an important part?

Items for Display

Semi-circular and circular protractor, devices that turn, spirit level, plumb line, clinometer, maps, sextant, nautical charts, compass, tiles for tessellations.

Activities

● Collect photographs and draw pictures of devices that turn

● From a scrap of newspaper make a paper right angle. Use the paper right angle to find other right angles in the room.

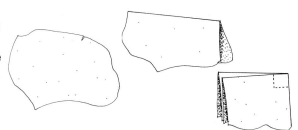

● Study shapes that contain right angles. What makes a square a square?
● Draw these shapes: square, rhombus, rectangle, parallelogram and kite. In which shapes do the diagonals cross at right angles?

● In a glass, the water always remains horizontal.

A hanging plumb line will always remain vertical.
Use a spirit level and plumb line to find horizontal and vertical surfaces.
Use a set square to construct and to find right angles.

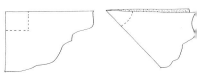

● Consider acute and obtuse angles, and list shapes that contain these angles.

● Fold in half a paper right angle to make a half right angle. (**SEE LINE DRAWING**)

● Find angles which are greater, less than, or equal to a half right angle.

● Draw a circle showing eight points of the compass. Face different directions and turn through right angles or half right angles, clockwise or anti-clockwise. Work out the new directions you are then facing.

● Use degrees to measure angles. 360° = one full turn 90° = one right angle
Use angles to create a secret message:

From H turn 90° clockwise to E,
then turn 180° anti-clockwise to?
then turn 360° anti-clockwise to?
then turn 45° anti-clockwise to?

The message is HE - - -

● Estimate the sizes of different angles, and then use a protractor to measure them. Construct angles of different sizes.

● Draw a triangle on a sheet of paper and cut it out carefully. Mark the angles 1, 2 and 3 and tear off the corners of the triangle. Place the angles together. What do you find?

● Try this with other triangles. What is the sum of the three angles in any triangle? Use the same method to discover the sum of the four angles in any quadrilateral.

● Use a Logo programme on the computer.

● Try to work out angles without measuring.

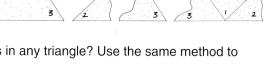

● Play paper snooker. Draw a variety of rectangles on squared paper. Imagine a ball being projected from a corner at an angle of 45°, bouncing off the edge of the grid at 90° and continuing to travel around the table until it reaches a corner pocket. For each rectangle, find out over how many squares the ball will travel before it reaches a corner pocket, and how many times the ball hits the side of the table. Is there a relationship between the dimensions of the grid and the number of bounces of the ball?

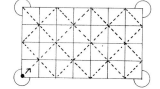

● Establish that a bearing is the angle measured clockwise between North and an object, always written with three figures. On a map, fix the position for a ship, and work out the bearings of different points (**SEE PHOTOGRAPH**). Plot courses for ships in channels. Fix a position in the playground, and with the help of a compass and circular protractor, work out the bearings of different points.

● Construct pie charts, for example, to illustrate a school day, use of pocket money, time allocated to different types of television programmes during a day.

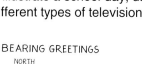

BEARING GREETINGS

NORTH

● Give bearings from the centre dot to send a message. For example, first word: 100°; 010°; 250°; 130°; 080°.

Symmetry

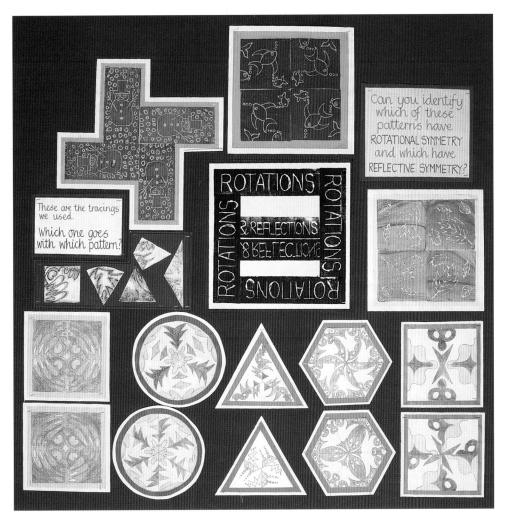

Discussion

Review the children's understanding of reflective symmetry. Look for reflections in water, mirrors, windows, spoons, etc. How many lines of symmetry has a circle?

Items for Display

A range of mirrors, including concave and convex. Pegboards and/or geoboards. 'Magic mirror' books. Shiny materials, such as aluminium foil, silver goblets and spoons. Reference of work by artists such as Escher, based on rotational symmetry. Scraps of wallpaper and fabric showing symmetrical designs.

Activities, Ideas and Investigations

● Sort and record 2D shapes according to the number of axes of symmetry. Cut out and fold, or use a mirror if any are unclear.

● Investigate symmetrical letters and create hidden messages.

● Using a selection of different shaped boxes with lids, investigate how many ways the lids can be put on each box. Using a young child's 'posting shapes' game, explore the number of ways that different shapes can be 'posted' through the correct hole.

● With partners, play games with pegboards based on creating a symmetrical pattern. For example, take turns in placing the pegs on either side of a marked axis of symmetry, the players gaining one point for every peg placed correctly. Extend this by using two axes of symmetry, when the second player has to place three pegs correctly to win a point.

● Investigate rotational symmetry by using 2D paper shapes. Number the corners of the shape, and then draw round it. Stick a pin in the centre of the shape and rotate it, finding out how many times it fits back into the original outline position. This number is known as the 'rotational order'.

- Draw windmills, using sails made from card and attached to a stick. Investigate how many axes of rotational symmetry windmills have. Design other shapes of sails and find their rotational order.

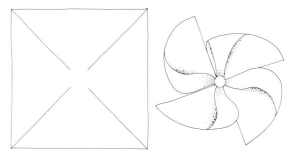

- Design and colour tiles showing rotational symmetry, either on paper or clay. Draw a square 12cmx12cm, and divide it into four smaller squares. Draw a simple pattern of lines in one quadrant. Trace this on to tracing paper, place the point of the pencil where the four dividing lines intersect, and rotate the tracing paper until the pattern lies in the adjoining quadrant. Trace the design down, and repeat for the remaining small squares. Colour the paper or paint the clay. **(SEE PHOTOGRAPH)**
- Repeat the above activity, using the same design, but use reflective symmetry, flipping the tracing over across the axes of symmetry. Are any of the quadrants the same as for rotational symmetry? Why? **(SEE PHOTOGRAPH)**
- Make a flat arrangement of five Multilink cubes. Draw round it on squared paper, and then rotate it 90° around one corner, drawing around it again. Repeat until it is back to its original position. How many rotations did it take? Investigate using different numbers of cubes. Does the number of cubes affect the number of rotations?

- Carry out investigations relating to transformations using co-ordinates in the four quadrants. Plot a simple shape in the first quadrant, writing down the co-ordinates, for example, (2,2) (4,6) (6,2) . Explore the effects of changing the sign (+ or -) of one or both of the co-ordinates - what type of transformation takes place? Try increasing the x co-ordinates by 3. What happens?

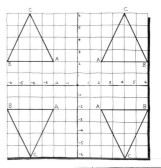

Point	1st quadrant	2nd	3rd	4th
A	2 , 2	2, -2	-2, -2	-2, 2
B	6, 2	6, -2	-6, -2	-6, 2
C	4, 6	4, -6	-4, -6	-4, 6

- Using the same co-ordinates again, investigate rotating the triangle through the four quadrants. Trace it, and, placing a pencil point at the *intersection* (o,o), rotate the tracing 90° into the second quadrant. Plot the triangle, and compare the new co-ordinates with the original ones. What has changed? Repeat into the third and fourth quadrants, after predicting how the co-ordinates will change this time.

Point	1st quadrant	2nd	3rd	4th
A	2, 2	2, -2	-2, -2	-2, 2
B	4, 6	6, -4	-4, -6	-6, 4
C	6, 2	2, -6	-6, -2	-2, 6

- Investigate folk and country dances which are based around symmetrical movements.
- Use mirrors to see how asymmetrical our faces are.
- Find line symmetry and rotational symmetry in different games, for example, Ludo, crosswords, chess.
- Study symmetry in nature - fruits, flowers, leaves, etc., and in art, for example, Celtic knots.
- Consider rotational symmetry in everyday life, for example, car wheels, screwdrivers, etc.
- Investigate symmetry in the process of printing. Try press prints, potato or sponge prints, lino prints, monoprints and screen prints. Print some fabric or wrapping paper.
- Make symmetrical patterns with a compass, and colour them to illustrate the symmetry.

Co-ordinates

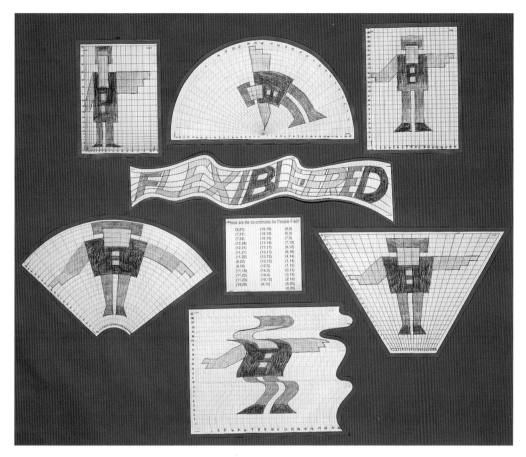

Discussion
How do we describe position? Consider the position of different objects in the classroom, for example, a child's desk, a light in the classroom, a picture on a display board.

Items for Display
Pegboards and pegs. Games which use co-ordinates, for example, Battleships. Maps of the local area, and beyond.

Activities, Ideas and Investigations
● Using the wall bars in the gym, or a climbing frame in the playground, one child sits or stands somewhere on the frame. That child's partner has to find a way to describe the other child's position. Now ask the same person to give their partner instructions to move to a new position, for example, 'Climb up to the third rung in the second column.' Draw a graphic representation of the frame and talk about a better way of describing position.

● Arrange the drawers and trays in the classroom using co-ordinates, for example, 'The white paper is in drawer (4,2)'.

● Make a spelling resource bank using the same principle of ordered pairs: 'The word you want to spell is at (3,5).'

4	their	important	dangerous
3	some	beside	beautiful
2	only	after	exciting
1	because	yesterday	weekend
	1	2	3

(5,4) (5,3) (4,5) (4,5) (2,3)

	1	2	3	4	5
5	B	J	P	L	Q
4	I	D	G	V	H
3	C	O	A	S	E
2	R	M	T	K	N
1	U	Y	W	F	Z

● Write secret messages, decoded by finding the letters given as ordered pairs.

39

● Play 'Battleships' and make up other similar games to play.

● Play 'Across and Down'. Use two dice, one red and one blue, and one 6x6 pegboard between two players. Mark the pegboard to show that the horizontal axis is represented by the red die, and the vertical by the blue die. Take turns to throw, and make an ordered pair from the score. Place a peg on the board in the position dictated by the die. The first to get three in a row is the winner.

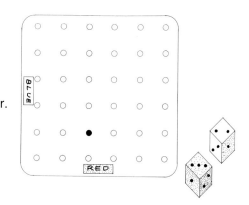

● Study the co-ordinates of regular shapes, for example, squares. Are there patterns to be found? Using this understanding, can you predict the shape which will be formed by plotting a particular set of co-ordinates? Can you write the co-ordinates which will produce a triangle, etc?

● Plot a simple shape of a person on a basic grid. Now try plotting it on to different types of grids. Ask the children to design grids to fulfil a given criteria, for example, where 'the legs are twice as long', or 'the head becomes wide and flat'. **(SEE PHOTOGRAPH)**

● Plot a regular shape on a grid, for example, a square, making a note of the co-ordinates. Investigate the effects of:
   – Doubling the x co-ordinate
   – Doubling the y co-ordinate
   – Doubling both co-ordinates
Can you find a way to double or halve the area/perimeter of the shape? What must you do to the co-ordinates?

● Plot the answers to multiplication tables by considering the answers to be ordered pairs, i.e. 7x2 = 14 = (1,4)

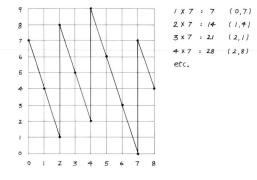

● Investigate the effect of pattern on ordered pairs, for example:

$y=x$	$y=2x$	$y=3x$	$y=x-1$
(1,1)	(1,2)	(1,3)	(2,1)
(2,2)	(2,4)	(2,6)	(3,2)
(3,3)	(3,6)	(3,9)	(4,3)
(4,4)	(4,8)	(4,12)	(5,4)

● Devise a set of co-ordinates that would produce a vertical/horizontal line.

● Plot a right-angled triangle in the first quadrant, and make a note of the co-ordinates. Investigate the effect of making one or both of the pair negative (*reflections*). How can the shape be made to *rotate* through 90°, 180° and 270°? What needs to be done to the co-ordinates to *translate* the shape?

● Study maps of the local area and find the co-ordinates of local features. Then, with given co-ordinates, find which place is at that position. Make up maps of a known or fantasy place, and devise games based on reading co-ordinates, for example, Treasure Hunts.

● Chess uses co-ordinates. Look at books and magazines about chess, and play computer chess games.

● Sew patterns on binka from written instructions. Write your own patterns.

● Using an outline of the human body drawn on a grid, give the co-ordinates of various organs.

● Study the relationship between an atlas and a globe, looking at the lines of latitude and longitude.

Enlargements

We used a grid system to enlarge these paintings.

The Snail
by Henri Matisse
copied and enlarged by James

Park near Lucerne
by Paul Klee
copied and enlarged by Lucy and Louise

Still Life with Basket of Apples
by Paul Cezanne
copied and enlarged by Simone

Discussion
When is it helpful to enlarge pictures or photographs? Does a shape change when it is enlarged? What instruments help us to enlarge? When would the police find it helpful to have enlargements of photographs?

Items for Display
Photographs and their enlargements, enlargements of sections of pictures, pantograph, magnifying glass, set of Russian dolls.

Activities, Ideas and Investigations
● Project a picture on to a screen. What happens to the size of the picture when you move the projector 1) nearer to the screen? 2) further away from the screen?
● Enlarge a slide picture by projecting on to a piece of paper and drawing around the outline.

● Study a simple picture enlarged to twice its original size. Measure to find out how the length of each side has changed. Note that the sides have increased in the same proportion.

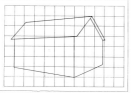
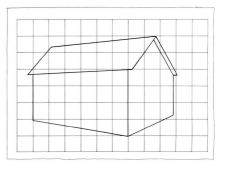

● Draw shapes on squared paper. Enlarge them so that the sides are 1) twice as long, 2) three times as long. What happens when the sides of a shape do not increase in the same proportion?
● Enlarge two simple shapes so that they are twice as wide but the same height.

- Enlarge two other shapes so they are three times as high but the same width.
- How does the area of a square change when you enlarge the square so that its sides are 1) twice as long? 2) three times as long? 3) four times as long?
- What happens to the area of a rectangle and a triangle when you enlarge the shapes in this way?

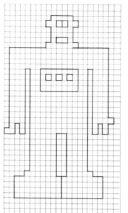

- Draw a shape on squared paper. Enlarge the picture so that all of the sides are twice as long.

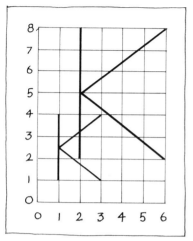

- Enlarge letters and shapes using co-ordinates. For example, the sides of the large K are twice as long as the sides of the small K. To obtain the large K, the co-ordinates of the points on the small K have been doubled.

- Find a method to enlarge a shape to four times its original size using co-ordinates.

- Cover a simple picture with a centimetre squared grid drawn on a transparent sheet. On a grid with squares twice the size, enlarge the shape, square by square, so that it is twice its original size. Use this method to enlarge a small picture to six times its size. **(SEE PHOTOGRAPH)**

- Mark a point P a convenient distance from the shape you are enlarging. Draw lines from P to the main points on the shape. Extend the lines so they are double their length. Join the ends of the extended lines to form the enlarged shape.

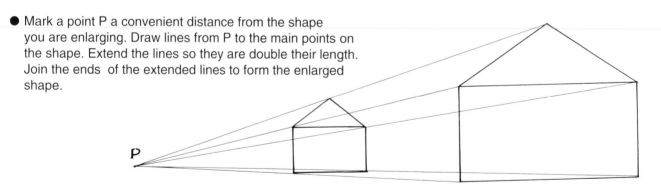

How many times the original size is the enlarged shape? What happens if the point P is inside the original shape?

- Use a method of your choice to enlarge a small area from a map.
- Draw some pictures of people in the hall of mirrors by enlarging them, for example, to twice the width but keeping the same height.
- A spy once sent a very important message on the back of a postage stamp. This was done by using a sharp pencil and looking through a magnifying glass so that the writing was very small. Try this method.
- Try to enlarge some of your handwriting to twice its original size.
- Investigate how your school photocopier or computer can enlarge letters and pictures.
- How does the length of the diagonal in a rectangle grow when the shape is enlarged to 1) twice its original size? 2) four times its original size?
- What happens to the angles in a triangle when the shape is enlarged?
- Pick a small leaf from a tree. Trace the outline on squared paper and enlarge the shape to three times its original size. Return to the tree and try to find a few leaves which are approximately the same size as your enlarged drawing. Does it appear that as leaves grow the sides increase in the same proportion?

Scale

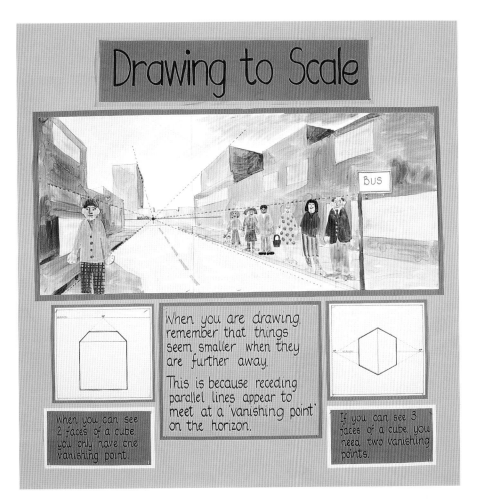

Discussion
What is a scale drawing? Why do we need scale drawings? What can happen if a picture or plan is not drawn to scale?

Items for Display
A selection of maps and plans. Plans of the school building. Large scale maps of the local area. Metre rule, rulers, tape measure. Carpet samples with costs, wallpaper book, clinometer, air line maps.

Activities, Ideas and Investigations
- Look at a variety of pictures that contain no people. How tall would you draw a person in different points on the picture to fit in with the surroundings? **(SEE PHOTOGRAPH)**

- Work out the lengths of real objects from pictures drawn to scale.

Pencil scale 1 to 3

- Work out the real lengths of other objects.

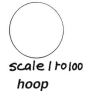
Screw scale 1 to 2

Worm scale 1 to 5

Rubber scale 1 to 4

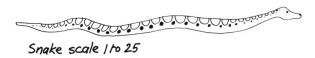
Snake scale 1 to 25

- Identify objects from pictures drawn to scale, for example:

scale 1 to 100
hoop

Scale 1 to 8
glass

Scale 1 to 15
plate

Scale 1 cm to 20 m
pond

43

- Choose a suitable scale to link drawings with real objects. For example, choose a scale for a rectangle to represent the following: 1) a box of chocolates, 2) a window, 3) a picture, 4) a lawn.
- Use a scale of 1 to 3 to draw your pencil. Use a scale of 1 to 10 to draw a whiteboard or blackboard. Use a scale of 1 to 20 to draw the top of a desk or table.

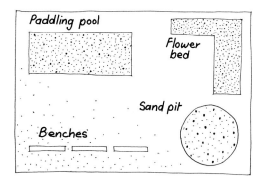

- From a playground drawing, drawn to a scale of 1 to 1000 (or 1mm to 1m), work out the approximate real measurements for the lengths and breadths of a pool, a flower bed, the length of a bench and the circumference of a sandpit.

- Draw a plan of the classroom using a scale of 1 to 100. Work out the size of paper needed for the plan. Do not include too many details.
- Draw a floor plan for an ideal house and a plan for the garden using a scale of 1 to 100.

- Find a large scale map of the local area and set a series of questions about the map, for example:
    1) How far would you drive from the post office to the church?
    2) How far from Joe's farmhouse to Bathsville Station?
    3) If you walk 100m each minute, how long will it take you to walk from the cinema to Bathsville Station?
    4) How far, as the crow flies, is it from the cottage to the cinema?

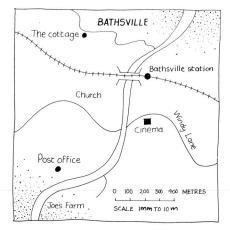

- Use a clinometer and a scale drawing to discover the height of a tree.

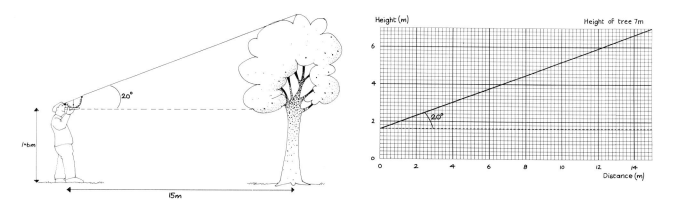

- Using a scale of 1cm to 50m, draw the plans of a golf course of your own design. The course should have 18 holes.
- Work out distances on maps of different scales. Plan an interesting car ride of approximately 100km starting and finishing at your school. Work out distances from home to holiday destinations.

Area

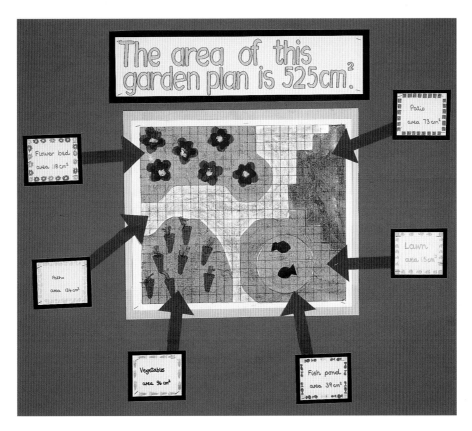

The area of this garden plan is 525 cm²

Patio area 73 cm²

Flower bed area 118 cm²

Lawn area 65 cm²

Paths area 134 cm²

Vegetables area 96 cm²

Fish pond area 39 cm²

Discussion
What does area measure? When is it necessary to measure areas? Can you compare areas by covering surfaces with 1) different shapes? 2) different sizes of the same shape? When would you measure an amount of surface using 1) square centimetres? 2) square metres?

Items for Display
A variety of shapes to cover surfaces, including squares, equilateral triangles, regular hexagons, regular pentagons, circles, rectangles.

Activities, Ideas and Investigations
● Discover which of two shapes covers the greatest area by placing one shape on top of the other.
● Compare the areas of larger surfaces by covering them with a repetitive shape, for example, a playing card. Estimate how many of these repetitive shapes would be needed to cover the seat of a chair. Then cover the seat with the shapes. What is the difference between the estimate and the measure?

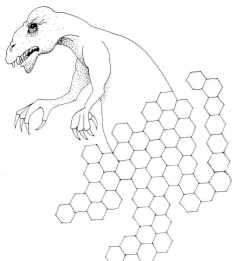

● Can a dinosaur be covered completely using 1) squares? 2) circles? 3) rectangles? 4) pentagons? 5) hexagons? Which of these shapes fit together leaving no gaps?

● On squared paper, draw five different shapes that have the same area.

● The best shape for covering most surfaces is a square. Count squares to find out how much surface is covered by different shapes.

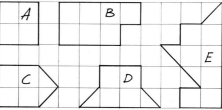

● Area can be measured in square centimetres. Draw some shapes on centimetre squared paper and measure their areas.

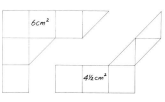

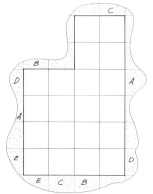

● Draw a shape on centimetre squared paper. Estimate its area by finding parts of squares that together are about the same as a complete square. For example: 20 whole squares, plus A+A=1, B+B=1, etc. Total area is approximately 29cm².

● After some rainfall, find a way to measure the area of a puddle in the playground. Measure it at regular intervals throughout the day and notice what happens.

● Work out the approximate area covered by your hand.

● Find out the easy way to work out the area of a square or rectangle using multiplication.

● Make a display showing several different shapes all with the same area.

● Plan a garden to include areas for flowers, vegetables, grass, a pond, a patio, etc. Specify how much of the area is used for each purpose. **(SEE PHOTOGRAPH)**

● Make some cut-out clothes for a washing line. Write the area of each item on the shape.

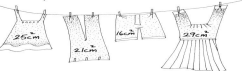

● On centimetre squared paper, draw and colour as many different shapes as possible that have an area of 6cm². Design some patterns for square floor tiles, each covering an area of 100cm².

● You can find the area of a triangle by drawing a rectangle. In the example shown, the area of rectangle = 8cm². The area of the triangle is half the area of the rectangle. Explain why the area of a triangle is ¹/₂ base x height.

● Try to discover an easy method for finding the area of a parallelogram using centimetre squared paper.

● Form a square with four one metre rules so that the area of the square is one square metre - lm².

● How many maths books can fit side by side inside a square metre?

● Name five surfaces in the classroom that would cover: 1) less than 1m²; 2) more than 1m²; 3) about the same as 1m².

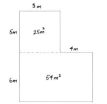

● Work out the approximate floor area of your classroom by dividing the floor into rectangles. Work out the cost of carpeting the classroom with carpets of different prices. Find the cost of carpeting rooms at home.

● Estimate the areas of five surfaces in the classroom using suitable units. Measure the area of each surface and work out the difference between your estimate and the measure.

● Try to make a cube or cuboid with a surface area of 96 cm².

● Draw a circle with a radius of 4cm. Cut the circle into pieces and use the pieces to form a shape like a rectangle as shown. Work out the approximate area of the circle.

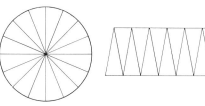

● Work out the surface area of paper in an exercise book.

● Investigate whether taller people have larger hands than shorter people.

● Work out the area of ground needed for 1) a netball court, 2) a football pitch.

● Work out a way to find the approximate surface area of an apple.

● Draw graphs to link area and perimeter.

Probability

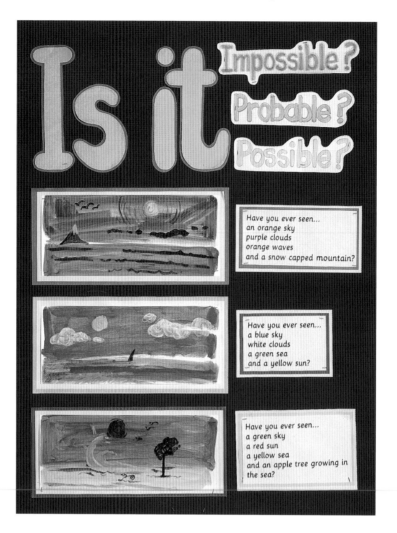

Discussion

Talk to the children about what is meant by *certain, impossible, unlikely, likely, possible*, and *50/50*. Think of examples for each one, for example, 'It is certain that I will be nine on my next birthday.' In order for predictions to be accurate, they have to be based on some experience. What is 'fantasy' and what is 'real'? What is the difference between fantasy and prediction? Why do people have lucky numbers? Are they really lucky? Some people say 'What can go wrong WILL go wrong' - is that true?

Items for Display

Selections of coloured items for investigations, for example buttons, dried butter beans dyed with food colouring, etc. Multilink cubes, etc. Dice. Logiblocks. Opaque bags for selecting items. A pack of playing cards.

Activities, Ideas and Investigations

● Sort events into categories (see Discussion). For example, 'It will rain tomorrow', 'I shall grow purple hair when I am l6'. Make drawings of *certain* and *impossible* events. **(SEE PHOTOGRAPH)**

● Put 19 yellow Multilink and one green Multilink into a bag. Pull one out. Is it more likely to be green or yellow? Or red?! Prepare bags to fulfil a given criteria, for example, 'Make it impossible to pull out a pink cube', or 'Make it likely that you will pull out a blue one'.

● Put five different coloured objects, for example, buttons, into a bag. Pick them out one by one, trying to predict what colour it will be. Do not return to the bag the ones that have been withdrawn. Do this ten times. How many times was your first guess right? Did your last guesses tend to be more accurate? Why?

● Record the outcomes of throwing two dice and adding the scores. Which total was obtained most frequently, and why? Use the scores to plot a track across a piece of squared paper: score 2-5 go left, 6-9 go forward, 10-12 go right.

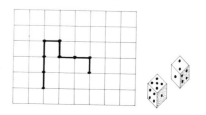

- Cover a die to make three red faces and three blue faces. Roll it twenty times and record the results. What happened? Repeat, using four red faces and two blue faces. What happens now? Predict the outcome when the die has five red faces and one blue face. Repeat the above investigation using a die with three different coloured faces.
- Guess how many times the word 'and' appears on a page of a book. Count. Try another page. Was your prediction more accurate this time? Why?
- How many ways can you find to colour a kite which is divided into four sections, using two colours? Try using three and then four colours. Can you predict how many ways there would be if you had a choice of five colours? Does this answer change if there is a rule that there cannot be two adjoining sections of the same colours?

- Using five flavours of ice cream, how many different four-scoop sundaes could be made? Supposing there was an optional chocolate sauce?

- During a football match, five goals were scored. How many different final scores could there be? How could these scores have been reached? (For example, 1-0, 1-1, 1-2, 2-2, 2-3; OR, 1-0, 2-0, 3-0, 4-0, 4-1, etc.)

- Use Pascal's triangle (see page 9) to investigate the probability of the outcomes of tossing coins. For example, when two coins are tossed, there are three possible outcomes in four arrangements: all heads (HH), all tails (TT), one of each (HT and TH). Therefore, the possibility of throwing all tails would be 1/4. What could happen when three coins are tossed?

- Look at Cardan's formula for calculating probability.
  This formula is: <u>Ways to obtain the desired outcome</u>
  All possible outcomes

- When ordering lunches for a school trip, there is a choice of two starters, four main courses and three desserts. How many different combinations could there be?
- How many different ways can five children arrange themselves to sit along a bench? Is this answer the same when they repeat this sitting around a circular table?
- Put a set of Logic blocks in a bag. Pick one out without looking. What is the probability of it being yellow? a yellow triangle? a small yellow triangle? a small thin yellow triangle?

8	12	1	9
5	6	●	2
4	11	3	10

- Using one 3x4 grid, each player arranges number cards from 1 to 12 in any order on his/her grid. Players take turns to throw two dice, add the score and place a counter on the appropriate number on their own grid. The first to get three counters in a row is the winner. After each game, players are allowed to rearrange their numbers so that they have a better chance of winning.

- Play 'Rock, Paper, Scissors, Stone', and the card game 'Cheat'.

Logic

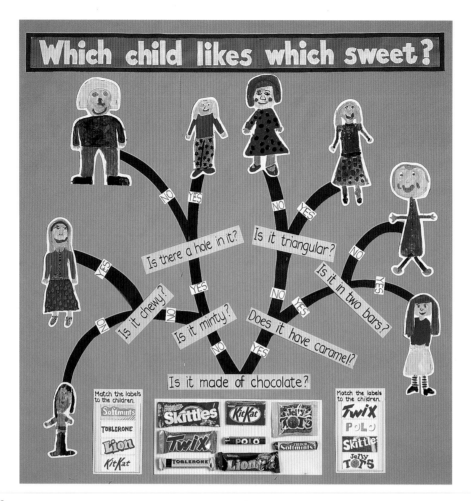

Discussion

Why do we sort things out? Talk about ways in which the class could be grouped. Play 20 Questions, to guess whom you are thinking of. Would it make things easier if supermarkets displayed their wares sorted by size or colour? Tell 'lateral thinking stories' and make up some of your own. For example, 'Someone who lived in a tall block of flats always took the lift to go down, but always climbed the stairs to go back home....unless he was with a friend. Why? (Because he was not tall enough to reach the necessary button.)'

Items for Display

Natural objects (for example, shells) for sorting. Structural apparatus (for example Logic blocks, Allsorts, etc.) Plastic set rings, or ribbon to make set rings. Blank Venn diagrams, Carroll diagrams, decision trees, matrices, mapping diagrams. Labels to use with these, for example, 'red' and 'not red'. Gadgets to help us sort - telephone directories, card files, personal organiser, alphabetical telephone index, concertina files, ring binders, etc.

Activities, Ideas and Investigations

- Sort objects by using Venn and Carroll diagrams, tree diagrams and matrices.
- Practise sorting, using given or own criteria. Include the concept of an 'empty set' by thinking of a criteria which would result in an empty set, for example, 'the set of children with purple eyes'.
- Reinforce the understanding of a negative attribute, for example 'not a triangle', by playing Simon Says: give negative instructions, such as 'Simon says, Do not put your hands in the air'.

- Play 'Attribute Dominoes', where the Logic blocks are placed next to each other according to the chosen attributes for that game, for example, 1/2/3/4 differences from the adjoining block. 'Star Dominoes' can be played in four directions at once, with anything up to four attribute differences, one for each direction.

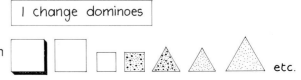

- Devise mapping diagrams, encouraging the children to:
  - enter the mapping arrows
  - complete one of the sets
  - deduce the meaning of the mapping arrow.

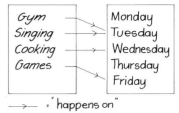

→ = " is the partner of "

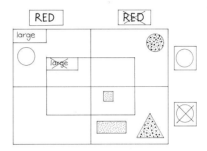

→ = " happens on "

- Make patterns with the Logic blocks.
- Choose a suitable attribute difference, for example, size. Ask a partner to make a pattern in accordance with the stated difference. Record through painting, printing or coloured gummed paper. Try with more than one difference, for example, colour and thickness.
- Make Logic block 'Attribute Machines' which work like function machines, where the shape is changed somehow before exiting. What was put into the machine? How was it changed?
- Sort items by using a decision tree **(SEE PHOTOGRAPH)** and a data handling program such as 'Branch'.

- Use Carroll Diagrams with several sections. Interpret the diagrams, and place the occupants in the correct sections.

- Reorganize the book resources in the classroom according to chosen criteria, for example, by author, by subject, by size, etc.

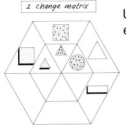

Use matrix grids to sort Logic blocks according to a chosen criteria, for example, two differences between adjoining blocks.

- Find as many ways as possible to sort a pack of cards.
- Produce a rota which ensures that everyone in the class does a fair share of helping to run the classroom properly, for example, sharpening pencils.
- Using a plan of the classroom, write the names of the children in the places where they sit, fulfilling given criteria. For example, 'Janine sits on a table near the door, with two boys', 'Nathan can look out of the window but is not allowed to sit near his friend Oliver'. Make your own plan and description - perhaps for animal cages in a zoo, or the layout of flowers in a garden.

- Play 'The Tower of Hanoi'. Using three different sized disks, move them from A to C. Only one disk may be moved at once, a large disk may not be placed on a smaller one, and a disk may not be taken out from underneath another one. What is the minimum number of moves to get 2/3/4/5 disks from A to C? Can you predict? Is there a pattern to the moves?

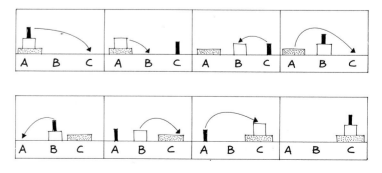

Graphs

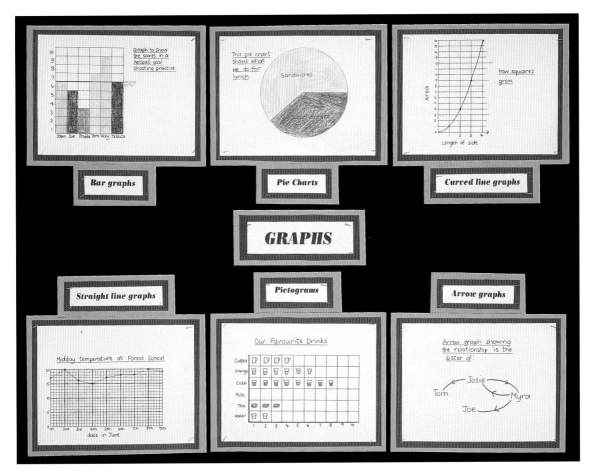

Bar graphs

Pie Charts

Curved line graphs

GRAPHS

Straight line graphs

Pictograms

Arrow graphs

Discussion

What is the purpose of a graph? Why do we use different sorts of graphs to display information? Where do you see graphs used for advertising? Can graphs be misleading? How do graphs save time? How do computers use graphs?

Items for Display

Examples of graphs used in advertising. Misleading graphs. A set of tables containing information and the resulting graphs for matching. Sets of graphs and associated question cards.

Activities, Ideas and Investigations

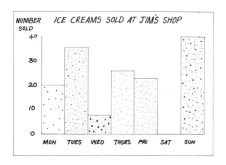

- Extract as much information as possible from column graphs, for example: Why do you think 1) no ice creams were sold on Saturday? 2) more ice creams were sold on Sunday than any other day? 3) very few ice creams were sold on Wednesday?

- Discuss how to choose a suitable scale for a graph.

- Draw a bar chart for teachers in the school. Write questions for the graph.

● Draw bar charts to show 1) the favourite cars of children in the class; 2) the distances of nearby towns from the school.

● Make a table showing the temperature at the same time each day. Record the results on a vertical line graph.

DAY	Mon	Tues	Wed	Thurs	Fri
°C					

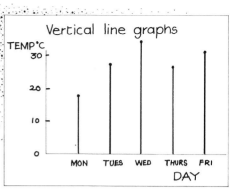

● Draw different graphs for some space characters to show their ages, heights, weights and lengths of nose. Make up some interesting questions for the graphs.

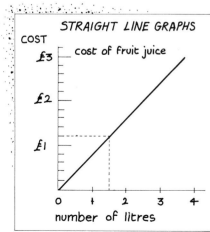

● On 'ready reckoner' graphs, every point on the line has meaning. For example, fruit juice costs 80p per litre. The graph shows 1½ litres would cost £1.20. Find the cost of 1) 2 litres; 2) 4 litres; 3) 2½ litres; 4) 3½ litres. Draw straight ready reckoner graphs which would help to find the cost of different quantities of 1) tea 2) coffee 3) sugar 4) potatoes 5) petrol.

● Draw a graph which would help to convert degrees Fahrenheit to degrees Centigrade.
● Draw a line graph to show how the perimeter of a square grows as the length of the side of the square increases.

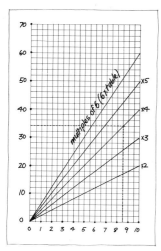

● Draw a graph on a larger sheet of graph paper and draw lines to show multiples for numbers up to 10. Every point on each line has a meaning. Use the graph to answer questions, for example, 7x9=?; 9x8=?; 8½x4=?; 9½x7=?

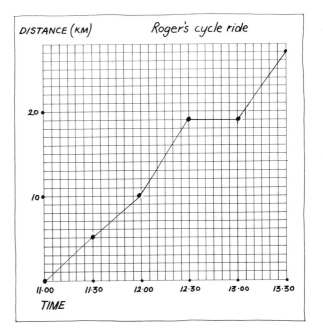

● Extract information from line graphs. For example: How far did Roger cycle? What was Roger doing from 12.30 to 13.00? During which half hour did he travel furthest? How far had he travelled by 12.00? At what time had he completed half the journey? What was his average speed?

● Complete a running, walking and hopping graph for yourself and one for a friend. What happens to the line on the graph as you travel faster? Work out your average speeds in 1) metres/sec.; 2) metres/min.; 3) metres/hour; 4) km/hour.

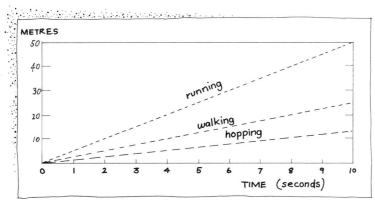

● Draw suitable graphs to show:
  – The different vehicles that pass the school in a set time. (Use a tally chart to help with the count.)
  – The difference in speed of growth of two bean shoots, one grown in a cool dark place, and the other grown in a warm bright place.
  – The height of the bounce of different balls when dropped from a height of 1 ½m.
  – The favourite authors of children in the class.
  – Pets owned by children in the class.
  – The lengths of reigns of kings and queens in England.

● Draw a pie chart to show how you have spent your time during the last 24 hours.

GAME 1 – **TAKE YOUR PLACE** (Place Value)

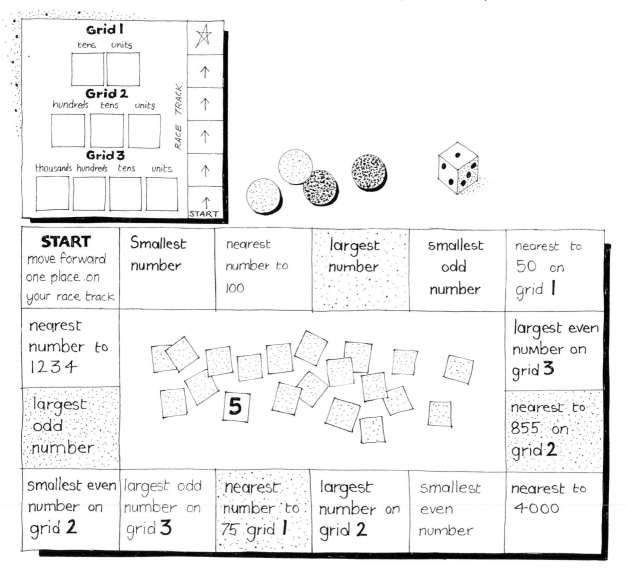

The game is for 2 to 4 players.

You need: A playing board (see above), a grid card for each player (see above), a set of two coloured counters for each player, a dice, a set of cards with two for each number from 0 to 9 (a dice numbered 0-9 can be used instead of a set of cards).

Rules:
Shuffle the number cards and place them face down on the table. Each player places one counter on the Start section of the playing board, and one number on the Start section of his race track on the grid card.

The first player rolls the dice and moves around the playing board the number of sections indicated by the dice. Unless instructed by the playing board, the player chooses one of the grids on the grid card for the first challenge. This player takes a card from the table and places it in any one of the sections on the chosen grid. Once placed, the position of the card cannot be changed. The second player takes a card and places it on the same grid, on his own grid card. Players continue to take turns until each player's grid contains a complete number. Players then agree who has won the first challenge, and the winning player moves his counter forward one section on the race track.

Play continues in this way until the first player reaches the end of his race track and wins the game.

The game is for two players.

You need: A game board (see above), 25 cards (numbered as above), two sets of 30 counters, three dice (numbered 1 to 6), or one dice numbered 1-20.

Rules:
Shuffle the 25 numbered cards and place them face down in a stack. The first player turns the top card of the pack and chooses to throw 1, 2 or 3 dice. The dice total is then subtracted from the card value to give the score. If the dice total is higher than the card total, the turn is missed. If the score matches one of the numbers in the boxes on the playing board, the player covers the number using one of the sets of coloured counters. Only one counter can be placed at each turn. Players take turns in this way until one player places five counters in any one of the boxes. This player is the winner. Players will need to choose between increasing the number of counters in a box and blocking an opponent.

When all the cards in the stack have been used, they are shuffled and replaced face downwards.

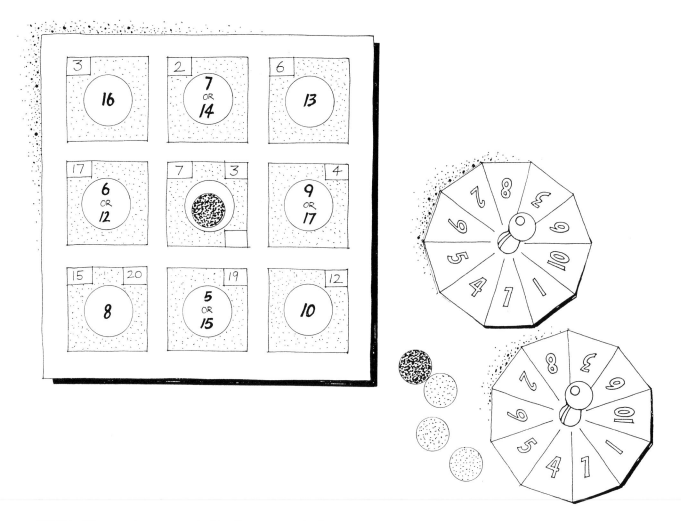

NOTE: The number concealed by the counter in the centre square is 18.

The game is for two players.

You need: A playing board (see above), two spinners and two sets of seven counters.

Rules: Each player uses one set of counters. Players take turns to spin both spinners. The score for each turn is obtained by adding together the two spinner numbers. Players continue to take turns whether or not they are able to use their score.

The winner of the game is the first player to form a straight line of three counters. Players can place a counter on a circle when a number in that circle is scored. Once a counter has been placed, an opponent can later remove this counter by scoring one of the other numbers showing in that square.

Example - If the first player has a counter placed as shown in the diagram, and the second player scores seven, then the second player can either place a counter on the vacant circle, or remove the opponent's counter.

The game is for two players.

You need: A playing board, a set of noughts and crosses, two spinners (numbered 1 to 10).

Rules:
The first player spins both spinners and multiplies the two numbers together. If the answer is showing on the board, the player covers this with a white nought. Only one number can be covered at each turn. The second player spins both spinners, multiplies the two numbers together and, if the number is on the board and not covered, the player covers the number with a white cross.

Play continues in this way until one player forms an unbroken line of four noughts or four crosses in any direction. This player is the winner.

GAME 5 – **COUNTER OPERATION** (All operations)

RACE TRACK

A												
B												

START ... FINISH

NUMBER LINES

36	64	50	45	16	24	32	6	12	18

8	36	42	20	56	18	10	40	15	21

32	30	14	18	28	12	80	4	90	72

The game is for two players.

You need: Number lines (see above), race track, 16 cards (four of each marked + - x ÷), two sets of 15 coloured counters, two spinners numbered 1 to 10 (numbered cards can be used if spinners are not available).

Rules:
Each player places one of his counters on the Start section of the race track. The operations cards marked + - x and ÷ are shuffled and placed face down in a pile. The first player spins both spinners and turns over the top operation card. If the spinners and card generate a number that is showing on any of the number lines, the player can cover this number with a counter.
(**Example**: Spinner numbers 6 and 8, operation card 'x' : answer is 48.)

At any time after placing counters on the number line, a player can choose to remove the counters in exchange for moves along the race track as follows:
   Two counters in an unbroken line can be exchanged for a move of one section along the track.
   Three counters in an unbroken line can be exchanged for a move of three sections on the track.
   Four counters in an unbroken line can be exchanged for five sections along the track.

Only one line of counters can be exchanged at any one turn. Players may not use extra counters, and if the complete set of counters is on the board at any one time, some of them must be exchanged immediately after the last counter is placed.

If, during the game, a player can block both ends of another player's line of one or more counters, the line of counters blocked is removed from the board.

For example: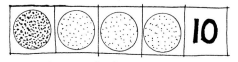

Player A has three counters on the board. Player B spins 2 and 5 and turns operation card 'x'. Player B places a counter on the '10', and removes Player A's counters.

The winner of the game is the first player to reach the Finish section.

The game is for two to four players.

You need: A playing card for each player, one dice, 16 yellow counters, 4 red counters, card or plastic coins: £1x16; 50px16; 20px16; 10px16; 5px16; 2px16; 1px16.

Rules:
Place all coins in a box lid. This will be called the bank. Each race is to buy one, two, three or four objects, as agreed by the players.

Each player takes one of the playing cards and places a red counter on the Start square. The first player throws the dice and moves round the board the number of squares shown on the dice. The player then takes the coin shown on this square from the bank. Players take turns to collect coins in this way using their own cards.

When a player lands on a BUY square, he must buy one of the objects on his card if he has the right money. To do this, the player puts the money into the bank and places a yellow counter over the circle in the section with the object.

The winner of the game is the first player to buy the agreed number of objects.

NOTE: If, on a player's turn, the coin shown in a square is not available from the bank, the player takes no money. Two 1p coins must not be taken in place of a 2p coin, and so on.

GAME 7 – **STEEPLECHASE** (Products and Factors)

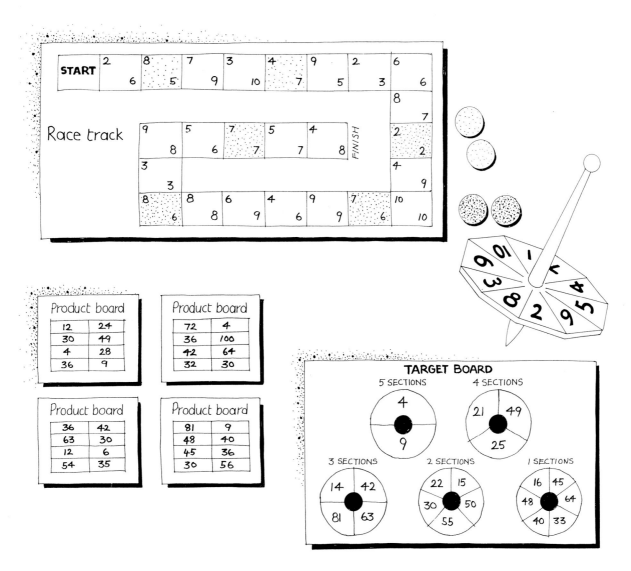

The game is for two players.

You need: Target board, race track, four products boards, two sets of two coloured counters, spinner numbered 1 to 10. (If no spinner is available, numbered cards can be used.)

Rules:
Each player chooses one of the product boards and one set of counters. Both players place one of their counters on the Start section of the race track. The first player chooses one of the targets and places a second counter at the centre of this target. The player then spins the spinner. If the spinner number is a factor of one of the target numbers, the player moves around the race track the number of sections shown above that target. If the spinner number is not a factor, no move is made on the race track.

Each section on the race track has two numbers. If the product of these two numbers matches a number on the player's product board, the player takes an extra turn.

Players take turns in this way until one player crosses the Finish line on the race track. This player wins the race.

GAME 8 – **FRACTION ACTION** (Fractions)

The game is for 2, 3 or 4 players.

You need: A playing board (see above), 20 fraction cards (see above), a different coloured counter for each player.

Rules:
The fraction cards are shuffled and placed face down in a stack. Each player places a coloured counter on the Start section of the playing board.

At each turn, a player turns over the top card of the pack. If either of the next two uncovered squares on the race track show a shape with this fraction shaded, or match the shape shown on the fraction card, the player moves forward to the appropriate box. If in either of the boxes the matching shape is shown with the matching fraction shaded, the player moves forward five boxes.

The winner of the game is the first player to reach the Finish box.

A player turning over a starred card has an extra turn.

61

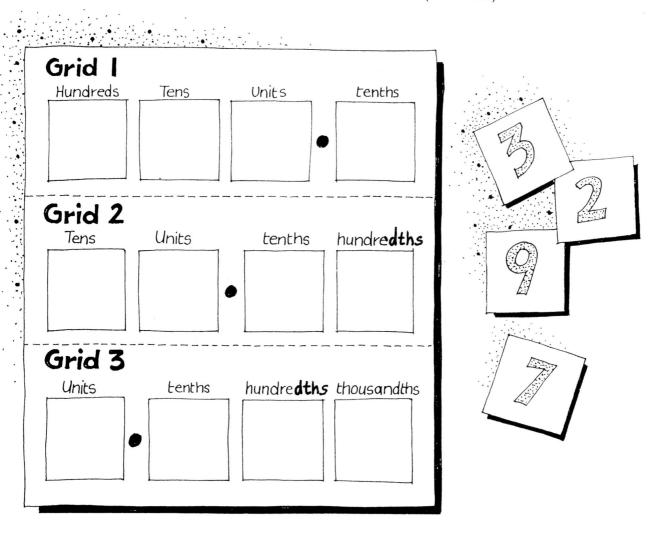

The game is for two, three or four players.

You need: A grid card for each player (see above), and cards numbered 0 to 10, to fit into the grid spaces. Six cards for each number is sufficient.

Rules – Game 1:
Each player uses one of the grid cards. The game can be played on 'Grid 1', 'Grid 2' or 'Grid 3', but all players must use the same number grid on their own cards. The object of the game is to form a higher grid number than any opponent.

The number cards are placed face down and shuffled around. The first player then selects a number card and places it in any one of the four grid spaces. The other players select cards in turn and place them on their own grids. On the second turn, cards are placed in any one of the remaining spaces. This is repeated for the third turn and the fourth turn. The player with the highest number is the winner.

If, during the game, a player selects a card number '10', one of the numbers on the grid must be multiplied or divided by 10 and moved one column to the left or right. The card is then placed to one side and the player takes another turn. If a 10 is selected on the first turn, the card is placed to one side and the player takes another turn.

Rules - Game 2:
As for Game 1, except the lowest number wins.

GAME 10 – **TAKE YOUR TIME** (Time)

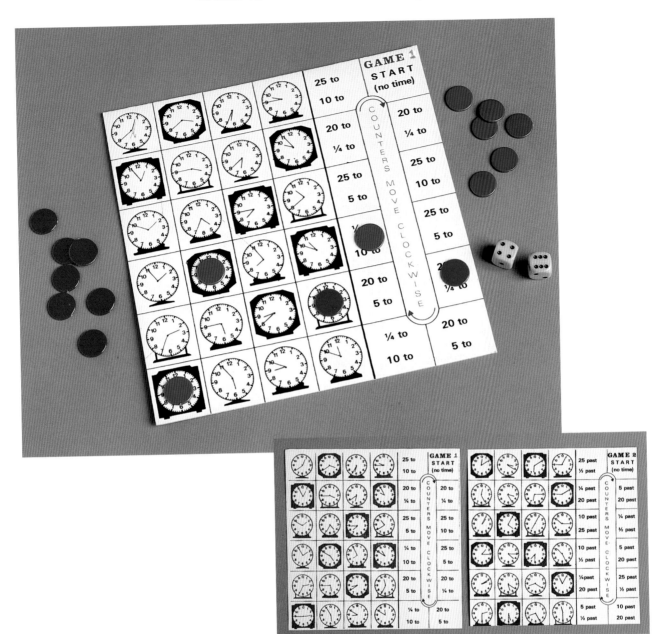

The game is for two players.

You need: A playing board (see above), two sets of nine counters, two dice numbered 1 to 6.

Rules:
Each player places one of his counters on the Start section. The first player throws one or two dice. The dice total gives the HOUR part of the time (a double counts as any hour). The dice total also shows the number of sections that the player moves his counter clockwise around the playing area. The section where the counter lands shows the MINUTE part of the time.

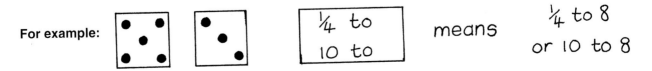

For example: [die showing 5] [die showing 3] | ¼ to / 10 to | means   ¼ to 8 or 10 to 8

If either time is showing on one of the clock faces, the player covers that square with a counter. Only one clock face may be covered at each turn. Players take turns to select times. The winner of the game is the first player to form an unbroken line of three counters, or to place eight counters on the board.

GAME 11 – **THE LONG DISTANCE RACE** (Length)

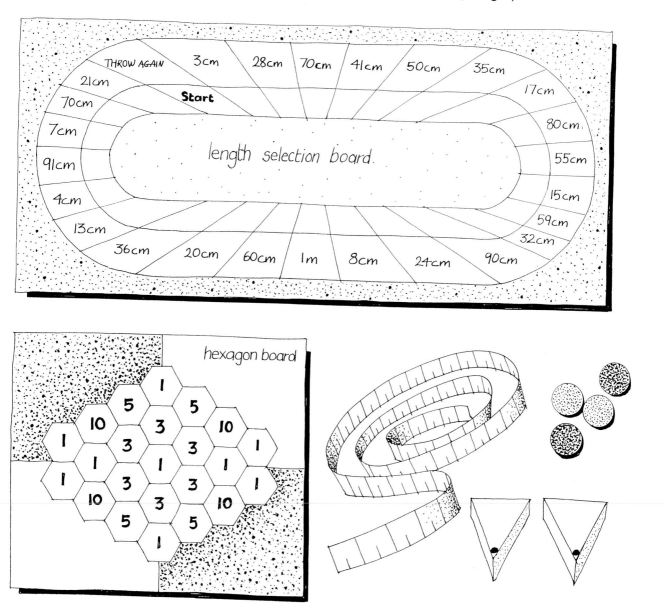

The game is for two players.

You need: Length selection board, hexagon board, tape measure or metre rule and 30cm ruler, two sets of 12 coloured counters, two markers.

Rules:
Each player uses a set of coloured counters. One of these counters is placed on the Start section of the length selection board. With the remaining counters, one player must try to form a pathway to link the two dark sections of the hexagon board before the second player links the two light sections of the board.

The first player rolls the dice and moves around the length selection board the number of sections shown by the dice. The section reached will show a length. The player estimates this length by placing the two markers at what is thought to be this distance apart. The distance between the counters is then checked with a tape measure. If the player has estimated the distance within 10 centimetres, one of the player's counters can be placed on a '10' on the hexagon board. If the estimate is within 5cm, a counter can be placed on either a '5' or a '10' section. If the estimate is within 3cm, a counter can be placed on a '3', '5' or '10' section. If the estimate is within 1cm, a counter can be placed on any section. If the estimate is incorrect by more than 10cm, the turn is missed.

GAME 12 – **WEIGHT WATCHER** (Weight)

The game is for 2 players.

You need: A scale, or scales and weights (10g, 20g, 50g, 100g, 500g, 1kg), two large counters, and two sets of 12 small counters, a dice (numbered 1 to 6), a playing board.

Rules:
Each player uses one set of coloured counters. The large counter is placed on the Start section of the playing board. The first player rolls the dice and moves the number of sections around the board shown by the dice.

The square reached challenges the player to find an object in the classroom with a weight between the two weight limits shown. The player weighs the object on the scales and if its weight is between the two limits, the player covers the square with a counter. The object cannot be used again during the game. If the chosen object is outside the weight limits, the player loses that turn.

Players take turns in this way, counting only uncovered squares as they move forward the number of squares shown. The winner of the game is the first player to cover three consecutive squares on the playing board, or who has eight counters on the board.

GAME 13 – **ANGLE TANGLE** (Angles)

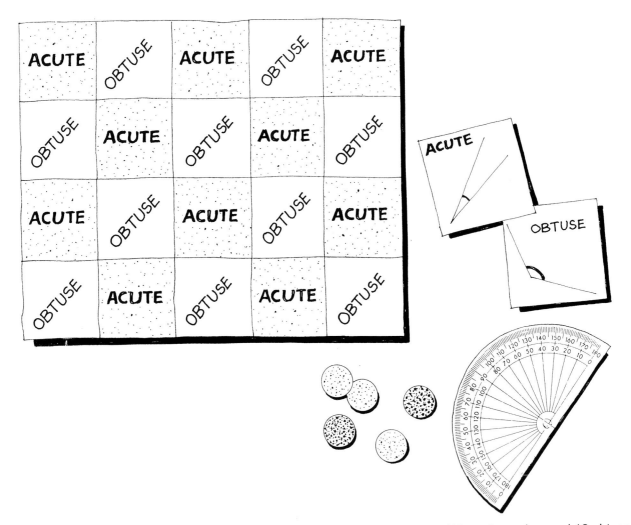

You need: A playing board (see above), 26 angle cards like those above (13 acute angles, and 13 obtuse angles)*, two sets of 15 coloured counters, protractor.

Rules:
Shuffle the angle cards and place them face down in a stack. Players take turns to turn over the angle cards and estimate the size of each angle (to the nearest 5^0 or 10^0 as appropriate).

If the estimate is correct, the player can cover a square on the playing board with a counter - acute or obtuse to match the angle card. The winner is the first player to form an unbroken line of three counters, horizontally, vertically or diagonally.

*Suggested angles for angle cards:
  Acute - 10^0 20^0 30^0 35^0 40^0 45^0 50^0 55^0 60^0 70^0 75^0 80^0 85^0
  Obtuse - 95^0 100^0 110^0 115^0 120^0 125^0 130^0 140^0 145^0 150^0 155^0 160^0 170^0

GAME 14 – **CO-ORDINATED** (Co-ordinates)

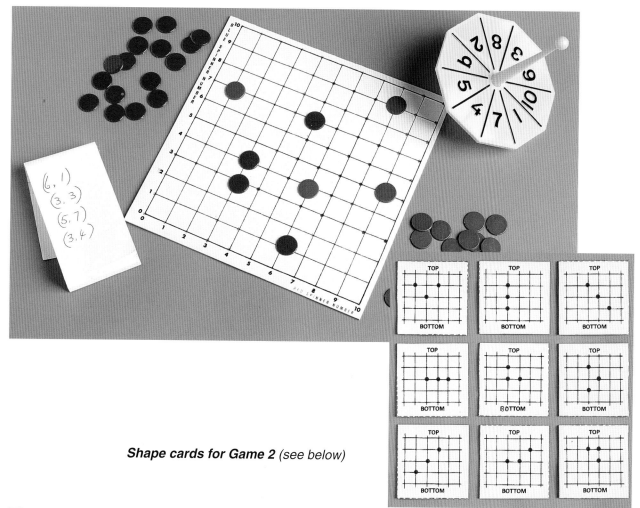

Shape cards for Game 2 (see below)

The game is for two players.

You need: Co-ordinates board, a spinner numbered 1 to 10 (or a dice numbered 0 to 9), shape cards for Game 2 (see above), two sets of 30 counters.

Rules - Game 1:

The first player spins the spinner. The number shown represents the number on the horizontal axis. The player notes this down. The player then spins the spinner again to find the number for the vertical axis. The two numbers give the co-ordinates of a point on the grid board, and should be recorded correctly.

For example: (6,3) - the player then places a counter on this point on the grid board (see diagram).

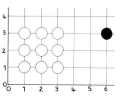

Players take turns to record co-ordinates and place counters in this way. If at any turn the player spins the same number on both spins, the point itself or any point next to it may be covered.

For example: after (2,2) any of the points circled in the diagram could be covered. When a '10' is shown on the spinner (or a '0' on a 0 to 9 dice), it can count as either '0' or '10'. If a player spins a point that is covered by an opponent's counter, that turn is missed.

The winner of the game is the first player to form an unbroken straight line of four counters.

Rules - Game 2:

Deal one shape card to each player **(see small photograph above).** The rules for the game are as in Game I, except that the winner is the first player to build, on any part of the grid, the shape shown on the shape card.

285	163	305	999	492
99	261	212	12	4216
5000	60	1956	33	6000
1001	2146	600	480	888
461	495	63	511	101

The game is for two players.

You need: A playing board, a calculator for each player, two sets of 15 coloured counters.

Rules:

Each player enters the number '100' on his calculator. The first player then presses up to three keys followed by the '=' sign, in an attempt to produce one of the numbers on the playing board. If this is achieved, the player covers the number with a counter. Whether or not the number matches, the new number becomes the start number for the player's next turn. Players continue to take turns in this way. The winner of the game is the first player to form a line of three counters horizontally, vertically or diagonally. At any turn, a player may choose to miss the turn and return to the starting number by clearing the calculator and entering '100'. If a decimal number appears on the calculator, the player misses that turn and returns to '100'.

The game can be varied by:
  a) changing the board numbers
  b) using a different starting number
  c) using a limited number of keys
  d) changing the rule for a winning pattern of counters.

The game is for 2 players.

You need: A playing board, 16 target cards*, 2 pawns, 6 red counters, 15 green counters, 15 yellow counters, a dice.

Rules:
Place counters on the playing board as follows: a red counter on each red dot, a green counter on each green dot and a yellow counter on each yellow dot. Shuffle the target cards and place them face down in a pile. Turn over the top card.

The object of the game is for each player to collect counters to match the value on the target card, and then to land on the escape hatch before his opponent. Counters have the following values: red 100, green 10, yellow 1.

Counters are collected whenever a player's pawn lands on any square containing a counter. At their turn, players move their pawns around the board according to the number they throw with the dice. Pawns cannot be moved diagonally or across fences (thick black lines) and although they can move in any other direction, they cannot visit the same square more than once at any turn. Pawns start on the appropriate Start squares. If a player collects counters which exceed the target card value, one counter can be returned to the board each time the player visits the Dump square. If a player is on the Dump square, he can miss a turn and return another counter to the board.

* Each target card shows one of the following numbers:
173   46   381   57   19   164   206   64
135   27   134   332 155   77   324   147

SUITABLE TEMPLATES TO CONSTRUCT NETS
(Drawn to size. Can be photocopied.)

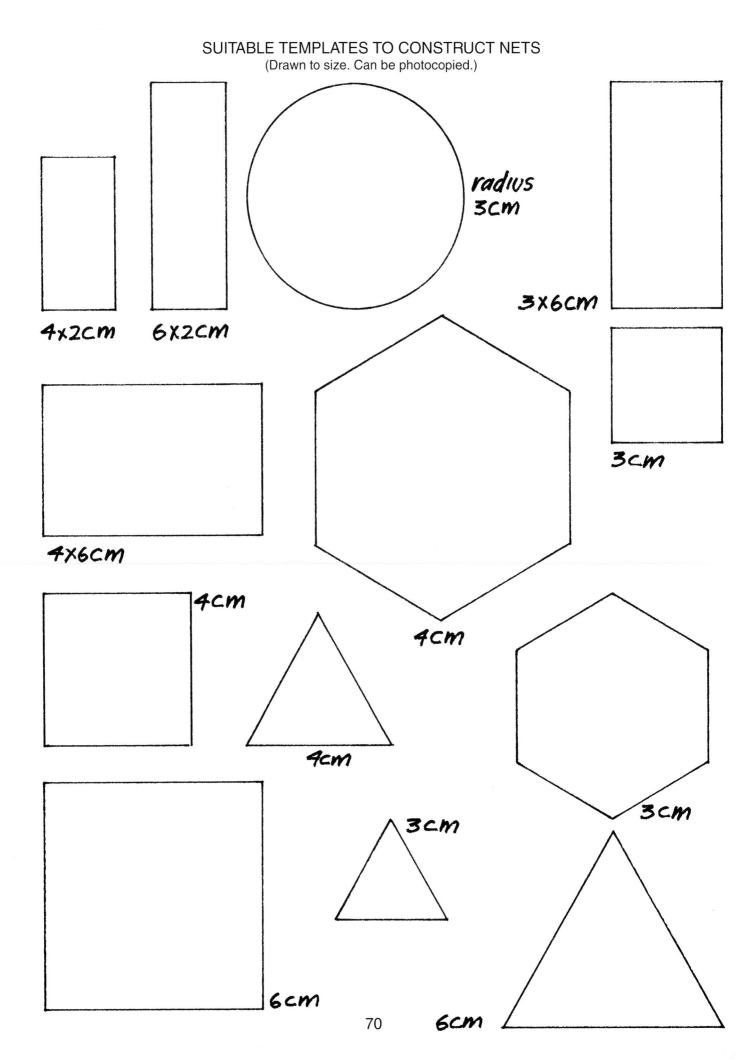

4x2cm

6x2cm

radius 3cm

3x6cm

3cm

4X6cm

4cm

4cm

4cm

3cm

3cm

6cm

3cm

6cm

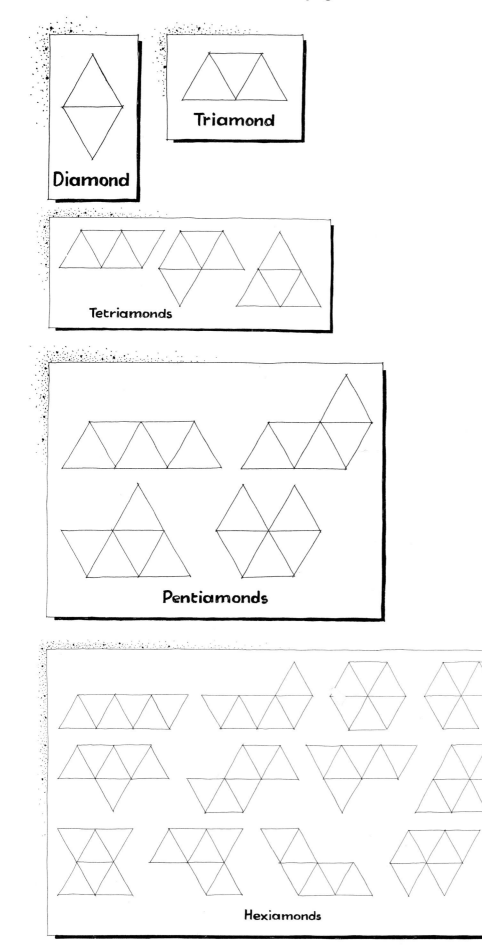

Diamond

Triamond

Tetriamonds

Pentiamonds

Hexiamonds

For details of further Belair Publications
please write to
BELAIR PUBLICATIONS LTD
P.O. BOX 12, TWICKENHAM, TWI 2QL,
England

For sales and distribution (outside North and South America)
FOLENS PUBLISHERS
Albert House, Apex Business Centre,
Boscombe Road, Dunstable, Bedfordshire, LU5 4RL,
England.

For sales and distribution in North America and South America
INCENTIVE PUBLICATIONS
3835 Cleghorn Avenue, Nashville, Tn 37215
U.S.A.

For sales and distribution in Australia
EDUCATIONAL SUPPLIES PTY. LTD
8 Cross Street, Brookvale, N.S.W. 2100,
Australia